From Music Hall To Tin P
Four Golden Decades Of Song

Part 1 1900s

Daddy Wouldn't Buy Me A Bow Wow
Daisy Bell
I Do Like To Be Beside The Seaside
I Wouldn't Leave My Little Wooden Hut For You
I'll Be Your Sweetheart
In The Shade Of The Old Apple Tree
Little Dolly Daydream
Love's Old Sweet Song
Nellie Dean
Sweet Genevieve
The Galloping Major
The Man Who Broke The Bank At Monte Carlo
Waiting At The Church
Where Did You Get That Hat?
Wot Cher! (Knock'd 'Em In The Old Kent Road)

Part 2 1910s

Ah! Sweet Mystery Of Life
Alexander's Ragtime Band
Any Old Iron
Blues My Naughty Sweetie Gives To Me
Don't Dilly Dally On The Way
Ginger, You're Balmy
I'll Take You Home Again Kathleen
If You Were The Only Girl In The World
Lily Of Laguna
MacNamara's Band
Memphis Blues
Moonlight Bay
Oh! You Beautiful Doll
Why Am I Always The Bridesmaid?
Your King And Country Want You

Part 3 1920s

A Garden In The Rain
Amapola
Baby Face
Baby Won't You Please Come Home
Can't Help Lovin' Dat Man
Dream Lover
Drifting And Dreaming (Sweet Paradise)
Honeysuckle Rose
I Can't Give You Anything But Love
I'll Always Be In Love With You
If I Had You
Louise
Miss You
More Than You Know
Ol' Man River
Show Me The Way To Go Home
Sweet Sue – Just You
That's My Weakness Now
The Lonesome Road
Together

Part 4 1930s

All The Things You Are
An Apple For The Teacher
Bye Bye Blues
Don't Blame Me
East Of The Sun (And West Of The Moon)
Falling In Love Again
I'm Gettin' Sentimental Over You
In The Chapel In The Moonlight
My Very Good Friend The Milkman
On The Sunny Side Of The Street
Pennies From Heaven
South Of The Border
Stars Fell On Alabama
The Touch Of Your Lips
The Way You Look Tonight
Underneath The Arches
Where The Blue Of The Night Meets The Gold Of The Day
Wrap Your Troubles in Dreams
(And Dream Your Troubles Away)

Wise Publications
London / New York / Paris / Sydney / Copenhagen / Berlin / Madrid / Tokyo

Exclusive Distributors:

Music Sales Limited
8/9 Frith Street, London W1D 3JB, England.

Music Sales Pty Limited
120 Rothschild Avenue, Rosebery, NSW 2018, Australia.

Order No. AM975018
ISBN 0-7119-9562-1

Printed in the United Kingdom.

www.musicsales.com

Music compiled by Peter Evans and Peter Lavender
Song background notes by Michael Kennedy

Text edited by Pearce Marchbank

Book design by Pearce Marchbank and Ben May
Text and image research by Katie Cornford

Printed in the United Kingdom by
Page Bros Ltd, Norwich, Norfolk

clusive Distributors:
sic Sales Limited
Frith Street,
ndon W1V 5TZ, England.
sic Sales Pty Limited
) Rothschild Avenue,
sebery, NSW 2018,
stralia.

der No. AM944152
N 0-7119-6597-8
s book © Copyright 1998
Wise Publications

ur Guarantee of Quality
publishers, we strive to produce every book
he highest commercial standards.
s book has been carefully designed to minimise
kward page turns and to make playing from
real pleasure.
ticular care has been given to specifying acid-free,
tral-sized paper made from pulps which have not
n elemental chlorine bleached. This pulp is from
ned sustainable forests and was produced with
cial regard for the environment.
oughout, the printing and binding have been
nned to ensure a sturdy, attractive publication
ch should give years of enjoyment.
ur copy fails to meet our high standards,
ase inform us and we will gladly replace it.

sic Sales' complete catalogue describes thousands
tles and is available in full colour sections by
ject, direct from Music Sales Limited.
ase state your areas of interest and send a
que/postal order for £1.50 for postage to:
sic Sales Limited, Newmarket Road, Bury St.
nunds, Suffolk IP33 3YB.

t the Internet Music Shop at
p://www.musicsales.co.uk

Wise Publications
London/New York/Paris/Sydney/Copenhagen/Madrid

Oh that peace may come. Bertie!
QUEEN VICTORIA'S DYING WORDS IN 1901
TO HER SON AND SUCCESSOR EDWARD VII.
(LEFT) READING HER OFFICIAL BOXES IN
1900 AT OSBORNE, ON THE ISLE OF WIGHT

It would really be more than English
could stand if another century began
and I were still alive.
OSCAR WILDE'S DYING WORDS IN 1900,
EXILED IN PARIS

A good, religious,
simpleminded Russian.
TZAR NICHOLAS DESCRIBING RASPUTIN.
(BELOW) 'THE MAD MONK' PHOTOGRAPHED
BEFORE HIS ASSASINATION IN 1916

Before Gibson synthesised his ideal
woman, the American girl was vague,
nondescript, inchoate...as soon as
the world saw Gibson's ideal it
bowed down in adoration.
THE NEW YORK 'WORLD' ON THE FAMOUS
GIBSON GIRL'DRAWINGS (FACING PAGE)
OF CHARLES DANA GIBSON

I can do one of two things.
I can be President of the United
States, or I can control Alice.
I cannot possibly do both!
TEDDY ROOSEVELT ON HIS
'GIBSON GIRL' DAUGHTER .
(LEFT) FATHER, BRIDE AND GROOM
AT HER GLITTERING WHITE HOUSE
WEDDING, FEBRUARY, 1906

Wedlock - the deep, deep peace
of the double bed after the hurley-
burley of the chaise-longue.
ACTRESS MRS PATRICK CAMPBELL, c.1905

The whole strength of
England lies in the fact that
the enormous majority of
the English people are snobs.

GEORGE BERNARD SHAW,
IN 'GETTING MARRIED', 1908
(ABOVE) A 'TYPICAL' ENGLISH
FAMILY AT AFTERNOON TEA

Lack of money is
the root of all evil.

GEORGE BERNARD SHAW,
IN 'MAN AND SUPERMAN', 1903
(ABOVE) FRENCH PEASANTS
BREAK FOR LUNCH, c.1904

Every cook has to learn
how to govern the state.
VLADIMIR ILICH LENIN, 1917.
(BELOW) GUESTS AT THE COURT
OF TZAR NICHOLAS c.1900

Poverty keeps together more
homes than it breaks up.
SAKI (H H MUNRO) IN
'THE CHRONICLES OF CLOVIS' 1911.
(BELOW) A 'RESPECTABLE' LOWER
CLASS FAMILY SIT DOWN TO
THEIR CHRISTMAS DAY TEA

'It won't be a stylish marriage,
I can't afford a carriage,
But you'll look sweet on the seat
of a bicycle made for two.

HARRY DACRE, FROM THE LYRICS
TO HIS HIT SONG 'DAISY BELL'.
(ABOVE) A 'CYCLIST'S RESTAURANT',
COBHAM, SURREY, 1910. BY THE END OF
THE DECADE THERE WERE 1.5 MILLION
CYCLISTS IN BRITAIN

Of all the trees that grow so fair, old England to adorn, greater are none beneath the sun than oak, and ash, and thorn.

RUDYARD KIPLING IN 'PUCK OF POOK'S HILL', 1906

Never again will I spend another winter in this accursed bucketshop of a refrigerator called England.

RUDYARD KIPLING IN A LETTER TO A FRIEND. (LEFT) THE GOVERNOR OF BRITISH UGANDA WITH HIS TROPHIES, 1913

Our civilization is still in a middle stage,
scarcely beast, in that it is no longer wholly
guided by instinct; scarcely human, in that
it is not yet wholly guided by reason.
THEODORE DREISER IN 'SISTER CARRIE', 1900.
A LIVERPOOL STREET, 1907; WATER WAS STILL
ONLY AVAILABLE FROM STREET PUMPS

If bread is the first necessity of life,
recreation is a close second.
EDWARD BELLAMY.
THE CRYSTAL PALACE c.1900. THE BUILDING
WAS MOVED TO SYDENHAM AFTER THE
GREAT EXHIBITION OF 1851, SET IN TWO
HUNDRED ACRES OF PUBLIC PARKLAND

My dear, I don't care what they do,
so long as they don't do it in the
street and frighten the horses.
MRS PATRICK CAMPBELL.
(RIGHT) RUSH HOUR ON LONDON
BRIDGE IN THE EARLY 1900's

We are healed of suffering only by experiencing it to the full.
MARCEL PROUST IN 'CITIES OF THE PLAIN'
(LEFT) THE SAN FRANCISCO EARTHQUAKE, APRIL 18, 1906

It is preoccupation with possession, more than anything else, that prevents men from living freely and nobly.
BERTRAND RUSSELL IN 'PRINCIPLES OF SOCIAL RECONSTRUCTION'
(RIGHT)MONTGOMERY WARD OF CHICAGO WAS THE FIRST MAJOR MAIL-ORDER FIRM, OVERTAKEN IN 1900 BY SEARS ROEBUCK

There is scarcely an hour when a staring wayfarer doesn't by his example collect a big crowd...no wonder people stare. A building 307 feet high with an edge as sharp as a ship's bow is well worth looking at.
'NEW YORK HERALD TRIBUNE', 1902.
(BELOW) NEW YORK'S FLATIRON BUILDING UNDER CONSTRUCTION

Form ever follows function.
LOUIS SULLIVAN IN 'THE TALL OFFICE BUILDING ARTISTICALLY CONSIDERED', 1900

"GREAT OAKS FROM LITTLE ACORNS GROW."

Montgomery Ward & Co. of Chicago

"A BUSY BEE-HIVE."
SECTIONAL VIEW OF THE ENORMOUS ESTABLISHMENT OF
MONTGOMERY WARD & CO.

History is more or less bunk.
It's tradition. We don't want
tradition. We want to live in the
present and the only history that
is worth a tinker's damn is the
history we make today.
HENRY FORD, QUOTED IN THE
'CHICAGO TRIBUNE'.
(BELOW) THE FORD MODEL-T FACTORY,
MANCHESTER, 1913

Nowhere to go but out.
Nowhere to come but back.
BENJAMIN FRANKLIN KING.
(LEFT) AS SPACE BECOMES EVEN
MORE LIMITED IN MANHATTAN,
THE NEW YORK SUBWAY OPENS
IN OCTOBER, 1904

Succes
Four flights Thursday mornin
Longest fifty-nine second
Inform press. Home Christma
TELEGRAM FROM THE WRIGHT BROTHE
KITTY HAWK, DECEMBER 19
(FACING PAGE) A 1908 AIRSHIP FLIES OV
CHEAPSIDE IN THE CITY OF LONDO

Laugh and the
world laughs with you,
snore and you sleep alone.
MRS PATRICK CAMPBELL IN A LETTER
TO GEORGE BERNARD SHAW IN 1912.
(RIGHT) THE SIX-YEAR-OLD BUSTER
KEATON IN 1901 WITH HIS PARENTS
IN THEIR VAUDEVILLE ACT

What is the Ninth Symphony
compared to a Tin Pan Alley
hit played on a hurdy-gurdy
and a memory?
KARL KRAUS, 1909
(BELOW) AN ADVERTISEMENT
FOR A NEW STATE-OF-THE-ART
GRAMOPHONE

The task I'm trying to achieve
above all to make you se
D W GRIFFITH, FILM DIRECTOR, 19
(FACING PAGE) SLIDES SHOWN
EARLY CINEMAS TO INFORM A
CONTROL THEIR PATRO

You can always tell when a girl
taking the Gibson Cure
NEWSPAPER COLUMNIST, EARLY 190(
(FOLLOWING PAGE) AN UNDERWE
ADVERTISEMENT FROM c.19

NEXT WEEK
THIS THEATRE WILL
HAVE TALKING PICTURES
TALENTED ACTORS & ACTRESSES
WILL BE BEHIND THE SCREEN.

Gentlemen will please refrain from
Smoking, Spitting
OR USING Profane Language
During the Performance.

LADIES
WITHOUT
ESCORTS
Cordially Invited

Ventilated
and
Disinfected
EVERY DAY.

Somebody's Baby is Crying
IS IT YOURS?

Don't Spit
On the floor...
Remember the
JOHNSTOWN FLOOD

When leaving
this Theatre
Please Turn
The Seat Up.

GOOD NIGHT

Daddy Wouldn't Buy Me A Bow Wow

Words & Music by Joseph Tabrar

Joseph Tabrar's catchy ditty was an immediate hit on the music halls from 1893 onwards for Leeds born Vesta Victoria. The composer was born in London in 1857 and wrote for many stars, including Marie Lloyd and George Leybourne, before his death in 1931.

love my lit - tle cat, I do, its coat is oh so warm, it

comes each day with me to school, and sits up - on the form. When

teach - er says, "Why do you bring that lit - tle pet of yours?" I

tell her that my bring my cat a - long with me be - cause —

Dad - dy would - n't buy me a bow - wow (bow - wow), Dad - dy would - n't buy me a

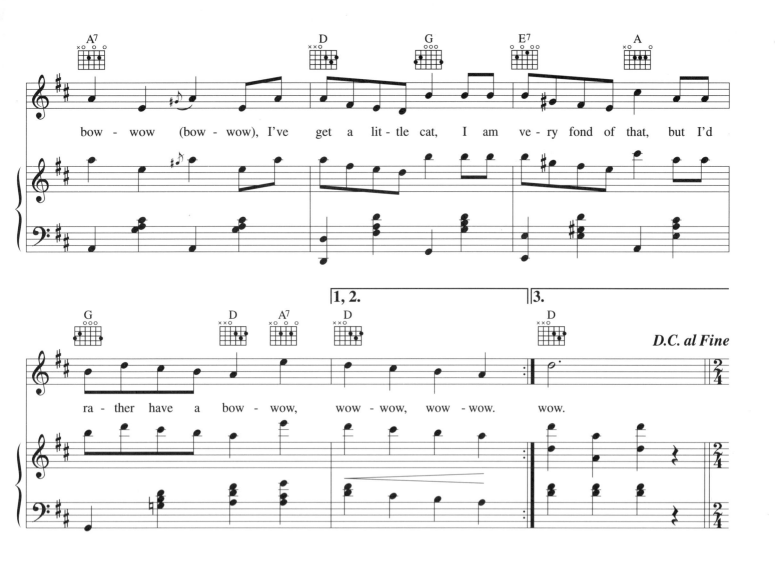

bow - wow (bow - wow), I've get a lit - tle cat, I am ve - ry fond of that, but I'd

1, 2.   **3.**

D.C. al Fine

ra - ther have a bow - wow, wow - wow, wow - wow. wow.

Verse 2:
We used to have two tiny dogs
Such pretty little dears
But Daddy sold 'em 'cos they used
To bite each other's ears
I cried all day – at eight at night
Papa sent me to bed
When ma came home and wip'd my eyes
I cried again and said –

Verse 3:
I'll be so glad when I get old
To do just as I please
I'll have a dozen bow-wows then
A parrot, and some bees
Whene'er I see a tiny pet
I'll kiss the little thing
'Twill remind me of the time gone by
When I would cry, and sing –

Daisy Bell

Words & Music by Harry Dacre

London born (1860) Harry Dacre emigrated to America where his greatest success 'Daisy Bell' (A Bicycle Built For Two) was introduced by vaudeville star Katie Lawrence in 1892. She brought the song to London and repeated her success on the music halls. Dacre returned to London, where he died, in 1922.

Plant - ed one day by a glanc - ing dart,

plant - ed by Dai - sy Bell!

Whe - ther she loves me or loves me not,

some - times it's hard to tell;

lyrics under the staff: you'll look sweet on the seat of a bi - cy - cle built for two! two!

D.C. al Fine

Verse 2:
We will go "tandem" as man and wife
Daisy, Daisy!
"Ped'ling" away down the road of life
I and my Daisy Bell!

When the road's dark we can both despise
P'licemen and "lamps" as well
There are "bright lights" in the dazzling eyes
Of beautiful Daisy Bell!

Verse 3:
I will stand by you in "wheel" or woe
Daisy, Daisy!
You'll be the bell(e) which I'll ring, you know!
Sweet little Daisy Bell!

You'll take the "lead" in each "trip" we take,
Then if I don't do well
I will permit you to use the brake
My beautiful Daisy Bell!

I Do Like To Be Beside The Seaside

Words & Music by John A. Glover-Kind

Blackpool Tower's famous organist Reginald Dixon adopted the jolly 'I Do Like To Be Beside The Seaside', by the Edwardian composer John A. Glover-Kind, as his signature tune. It was featured in the film The Adventures Of Sherlock Holmes and was a favourite for music hall legend Florrie Forde.

Con spirito

1. Ev - er - y - one de - lights to spend their sum - mer's ho - li -
(Verses 2 & 3 see block lyric)

day,＿＿＿ down be - side the side of the sil - ver - y

quite a no - ve - ty, _____ I save up all the mo - ney I can while

win - ter's grim and grey, _____ then off I run to

have some fun where the bal - my bree - zes play. Oh! I

do like to be be - side the sea - side, _____ I

Verse 2:
Timothy went to Blackpool for the day last Eastertide
To see what he could see by the side of the sea
Soon as he reached the station there the first thing he espied
Was the wine lodge door stood open invitingly
To quench his thirst he toddled inside and called out for a
'wine'
Which grew to eight or nine 'til his nose began to shine
Said he "What people see in the sea I'm sure I fail to see"
So he caught the train back home again, then to his wife said
he:

Verse 3:
William Sykes the burglar he'd been out to work one night
Filled his bag with jewels, cash and plate
Constable Brown felt quite surprised when William hove in sight
Said he "The hours you're keeping are far too late"
So he grabbed him by the collar and lodged him safe and sound in
jail
Next morning looking pale Bill told a tearful tale
The Judge said "For a couple of months, I'm sending you away."
Said Bill "How kind! Well if you don't mind where I spend my
holiday."

I Wouldn't Leave My Little Wooden Hut For You

Words & Music by Tom Mellor & Charles Collins

Once on a can-ni-bal isle there dwelt a dark - eyed maid;

lived all a-lone in her lit-tle log hut in the palm - tree's

30

Verse 2:

Just then some cannibals came in sight with swords and spears
Longing for something for supper that night - making ugly leers.
That Queen said, "Stranger, you'd better go;
That chief in war paint, you see, is my beau."

"Oh! is that true?" he said, as to'ards the stream he fled
And jump'd into a boat afloating there:
He was soon clean out of sight.
He won't return again just to hear that girl explain.

I'll Be Your Sweetheart

Words & Music by Harry Dacre

1. One day I saw two lov-ers in a
(Verses 2 & 3 see block lyric)

gar - den, a lit - tle lad and lass with gold - en hair. They

looked as sweet as hon - ey in a bee - hive and so I stood and watched the youth - ful

pair, the lad all blush - ing gave the maid a kiss, then

ten - der - ly he whis - pered this.

I'll be your sweet - heart

Verse 2:
The blue bells were accepted by the maiden
She said "I'll keep them safely all my life
But then suppose you meet some other lady
And I should never be your darling wife
He shook his head and took another kiss
Then once again he whispered this:

Verse 3:
The years flew by and once again I saw them
They stood before the alter hand in hand
A handsome pair I never shall forget them
The happiest young couple in the land
And once again he took the loving kiss
Then passionately whispered this:

In The Shade Of
The Old Apple Tree

Words & Music by Egbert Van Alstyne & Harry Williams

The 1905 hit 'In The Shade Of The Old Apple Tree' was originally a success for Charles Holland in music hall days. Its composer, Boston born Egbert Van Alstyne, became a song plugger in New York where he teamed up with Harry Williams. They worked together as a vaudeville team singing their hits - including this one.

tune, the vil - lage bells at noon were gai - ly

ring - ing, the world seem'd bright - er than a har - vest

moon; for there with - in my arms I gent - ly

pressed you, and blush - ing red, you slow - ly turned a

voice that I heard, like the song of the bird, seem'd to

whis - per sweet mu - sic to me; _____ I could

hear the dull buzz of the bee, _____ in the

blos - soms as you said to me, _____ with a

heart that is true, I'll be wait - ing for you, on the

shade of the old ap - ple tree.

D.C.

Verse 2:
I've really come a long way from the city
And though my heart is breaking I'll be brave
I've brought this bunch of flow'rs I think they're pretty
To place upon a freshly moulded grave;

If you will show me, father, where she's lying
Or if it's far just point it out to me
Said he "She told us all when she was dying
To bury her beneath the apple tree."

Little Dolly Daydream

Words & Music by Leslie Stuart

Leslie Stuart (real name Thomas Augustine Barratt) from Southport, Lancashire, wrote 'Little Dolly Daydream' for blackface singer Eugene Stratton in 1897 and achieved similar success with 'Lily Of Laguna' and his score for the extremely successful musical comedy Florodora.

Moderato

1. I've
(Verse 2 see block lyric)

wait - ed long to have ma say, till South - ern garls have

had deir day, I've got de smile now all de while now

just a-no-der mai-dy come to stay._____ Dose garls way down would

get no show, Dey'd stand no chance in I-da-ho; She

ain't no pic-ca-nin-ny from way-down or West Vir-gin-ny. But

Pride of I - da-ho, so now ye know,_____ and when ye go,_____ ye'll see there's

some - thin' on her mind; don't think it's you, 'kase

no one's got to kiss dat garl but me! me!_____

Verse 2:
I ain't spoke yet, nor her to me
But lor! ye purty soon can see
She's only waitin' for me statin'
Dat I'm just as much in lub as she.

Dere's one poor cuss, she fools him so
He tells dem all round Idaho
Dat he's her best intended
Bekase deir styles has blended
But she fools wid him to send my jealous on de go.

Love's Old Sweet Song

Words by J. Clifton Bingham
Music by James L. Molloy

'Love's Old Sweet Song', also known by the first line of its chorus 'Just A Song At Twilight', was written by the Irish composer James Lyman Molloy, who studied law and was appointed secretary to the Attorney General. Although born in 1835, he wrote his first song in 1863. This one dates from 1884 and is the most popular. It was introduced by Annette Sterling.

Moderato

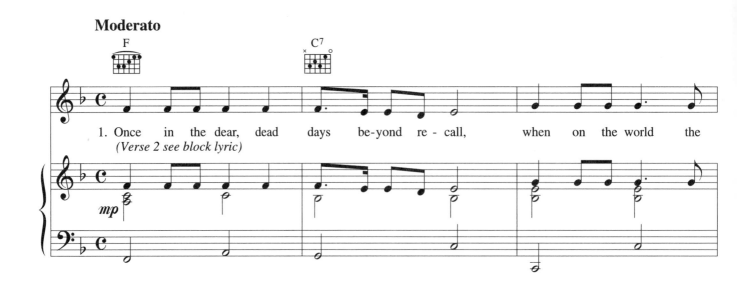

1. Once in the dear, dead days be-yond re-call, when on the world the
(Verse 2 see block lyric)

mists be-gan to fall, out of the dreams that rose in hap-py throng,

low to our hearts love sang an old sweet song, and in the dusk where

fell the fire-light gleam, soft-ly it wove it-self in-to our dream.

Just a song at twi-light, when the lights are low;

and the flick-'ring shad-ows, soft-ly come and go. Tho' the heart be

Verse 2:
Even today we hear love's song of yore
Deep in our hearts it swells forever-more
Foorsteps may falter
Weary grow the way
Still we can hear it at the close of day
So 'til the end when life's dim shadows fall
Love will be found the sweetest song of all.

The Man Who Broke The Bank At Monte Carlo

Words & Music by Fred Gilbert

A former child actor, Fred Gilbert originally had difficulty placing this song with a suitable singer. Albert Chevalier rejected it, but Charles Coborn after a similar rejection, slept on it, and finally bought it. The song made his fortune on stage, and he sang it in at least two films. In the USA, William Hoey also enjoyed a huge success with the song.

For-tune smil'd up-on me as she'd nev-er done be-fore, and I've

now such lots of mo-ney, I'm a gent. Yes, I've

now such lots of mo-ney, I'm a gent. As I

walk a-long the *Bois Boo-long,* with an in-de-pen-dent air, you can

50

Verse 2:
I stay indoors till after lunch, and then my daily walk
To the great Triumphal Arch is one grand Triumphal march
Observ'd by each observer with the keenness of a hawk
I'm a mass of money, linen, silk and starch.
I'm a mass of money, linen, silk and starch.

Verse 3:
I patronized the tables at the Monte Carlo hell
Till they hadn't got a sou for a Christian or a Jew
So I quickly went to Paris for the charms of mad'moiselle
Who's the loadstone of my heart – What can I do
When with twenty tongues she swears that she'll be true?

Nellie Dean

Words & Music by Harry Armstrong

Harry Armstrong, from Somerville Massachusetts, specialised in Edwardian ballads. 'Sweet Adeline' was a major success in 1896. In 1905 came 'Nellie Dean', beloved of pub pianists and barber shop quartets. The composer was first a boxer, then a music publisher - not an obvious progression, perhaps.

Andante moderato

1. By the old mill stream I'm dream-ing, Nel - lie
(Verse 2 see block lyric)

Dean, dream-ing of your bright eyes gleam-ing, Nel - lie Dean. As they

seem to sing of you with your ten - der eyes of blue, for I

know they miss you too, Nel - lie Dean. *Chorus* There's an

old mill by the stream, Nel - lie Dean, where we

used to sit and dream, Nel - lie Dean. And the

54

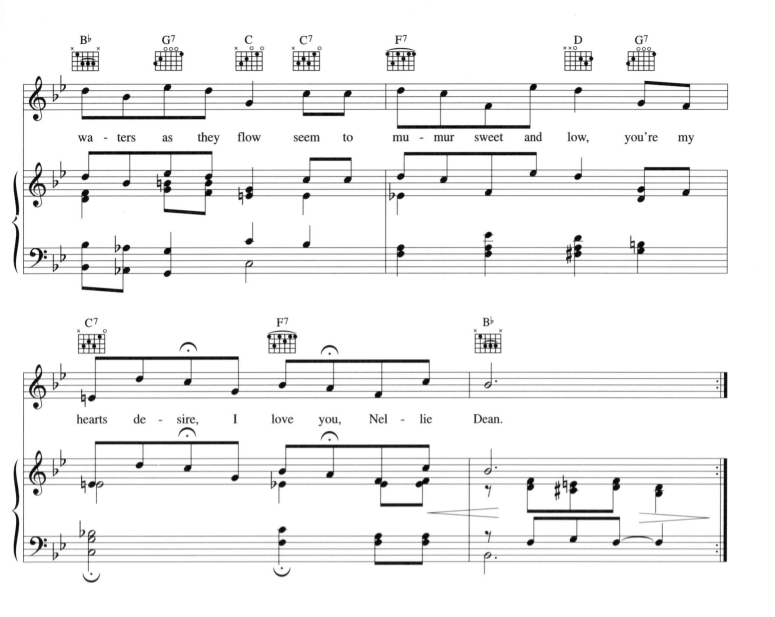

waters as they flow seem to mu-mur sweet and low, you're my

hearts de-sire, I love you, Nel-lie Dean.

Verse 2:
I recall the day we parted, Nellie Dean
How you trembled, broken hearted, Nellie Dean
And you pinned a rose of red
On my coat of blue and said
That a soldier boy you'd wed, Nellie Dean.

All the world seems sad and lonely, Nellie Dean
For I love you and you only, Nellie Dean.
And I wonder if on high
You still love me if you sigh
For the happy days are gone by, Nellie Dean.

The Galloping Major

Words & Music by G. Bastow & F. W. Leigh

Allegretto

Repeat until ready

N.C.   G

G

1. When I was in the ar - my I was a cav - al - ry man, you
(Verses 2 & 3 see block lyric)

D7

know,_____ and when - ev - er I went on pa - rade_____ a mag -

57

Verse 2:

Last year I thought I'd treat myself to a holiday by the sea

So I went, and my quarters I fixed

Then I found that the bathing was mixed.

So I gallop'd away to a bathing machine

In the busiest part of the day

And I soon felt at home with the girls in the water

And join'd in their frivolous play.

They were beautiful creatures, but lor!

How they giggled as soon as they saw *me*

Verse 3:

I always was a ladies man and a favourite with the sex

Well, I called upon one yesterday

Though I won't give the lady away.

She started to talk of my army career

And was quite interested, you see

But I got rather tired, so we talk'd about her

Which was more interesting to me.

And she said I'd been taking some wine

For as soon as we sat down to dine *I went*

Sweet Genevieve

Words & Music by George Cooper & Henry Tucker

Slow with expression

1. O Ge-ne-vieve, I'd give the world to
(Verse 2 see block lyric)

live a-gain the love-ly past! The rose of youth is

dew-im-pearl'd, but now it with-ers in the blast. I

days may come, the days— may go, but still the hands of

mem - 'ry weave the bliss - ful dreams of long a - go.

Verse 2:

Fair Genevieve, my early love!
The years but make thee dearer far
My heart shall never, never rove
Thou art my only guiding star.

For me the past has no regret
Whate'er the years may bring to me
I bless the hour when first we met
The hour that gave me love and thee!

Where Did You Get That Hat?

Words & Music by Jos. J Sullivan

It may not be immediately obvious but composer Joseph Sullivan based his catchy song on themes from Wagner's Lohengrin and Die Meistersinger. The vaudeville artiste/composer, rummaging in an old trunk, found an old hat that caused much amusement. He introduced the song at the Miners Eighth Avenue Theater, New York in 1888.

how I came to get this hat, 'tis ve-ry strange and fun-ny,
(Verses 2-5 see block lyric)

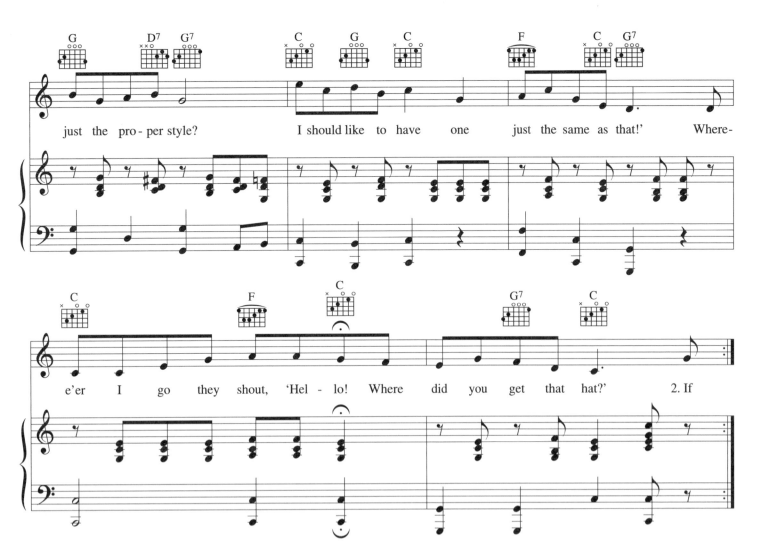

just the pro-per style? I should like to have one just the same as that!' Where-

e'er I go they shout, 'Hel-lo! Where did you get that hat?' 2. If

Verse 2:
If I go to the op'rahouse, in the op'ra season
There's someone sure to shout at me without the slightest reason
If I go to a Concert Hall to have a jolly spree
There's someone in the party who is sure to shout at me:

Verse 3:
At twentyone I thought I would to my sweetheart get married
The people in the neighbourhood had said too long we'd tarried
So off to church we went right quick determined to get wed
I had not long been in there, when the parson to me said:

Verse 4:
I once tried hard to me be M.P., but failed to get elected
Upon a tub I stood, round which a thousand folks collected
And I had dodged the eggs and bricks (which was no easy task)
When one man cried, 'A question I the candidate would ask!'

Verse 5:
When Colonel South, the millionaire, gave his last garden party
I was amongst the guests who had a welcome true and hearty
The Prince of Wales was also there, and my heart jump'd with glee
When I was told the Prince would like to have a word with me.

Spoken after 1st verse. – And everywhere I go – everyone shouts after me –
Spoken after 4th verse. – I told him that I was ready to reply to any question that could be put to me. The man said – "Thousands of British working people are anxiously awaiting enlightenment on the subject on which I am about to address you. It is a question of national importance, in fact; THE great problem of the day – and that is, Sir –
Spoken after 5th verse. – I was duly presented to His Royal Highness, who immediately exclaimed –

Waiting At The Church

Words & Music by Fred Leigh & Henry Pether

'Can't get away to marry you today - my wife won't let me!' - the final revelatory twist in one of the most popular of all music hall songs was another smash hit for the beloved Vesta Victoria. It was written in 1906 and had a welcome revival in the Bing Crosby/Mary Martin picture The Birth Of The Blues.

Allegro moderato

1. I'm in a nice bit of trou - ble, I con - fess;
(Verses 2 & 3 see block lyric)

some - bo - dy with me has had a game. I should by now be a

proud and hap - py bride, but I've still got to keep my sin - gle

name. I was pro-posed to by O - ba - di - ah Binks

in a ve - ry gen - tle-man - ly way;

lent him all my mo - ney so that he could buy a home, and

Verse 2:
Lor, what a fuss Obadiah made of me
When he used to take me in the park!
He used to squeeze me till I was black and blue
When he kissed me he used to leave a mark.

Each time he met me he treated me to port
Took me now and then to see the play
Understand me rightly, when I say he treated me
It wasn't *him* but *me* that used to pay.

Verse 3:
Just think of how disappointed I must feel
I'll be off my crumpet very soon.
I've lost my husband the one I never had!
And I dreamed so about the honeymoon.

I'm looking out for another Obadiah
I've already bought the wedding ring
There's all my little fal-the-riddles packed up in my box–
Yes, absolutely two of ev'rything.

Wot Cher!
(Knock'd 'Em In The Old Kent Road)

Words & Music by Charles Ingle

Last week

Repeat until ready

down our al - ley come a toff, nice old geez - er with a nas - ty cough,

sees my Mis - sus, takes 'is top - per off, in a ve - ry gen - tle-man - ly

way! "Ma'am" says he, "I have some news to tell,

your rich Un - cle Tom of Cam - ber-well, popped off

re - cent, which it ain't a sell. Leav - ing you 'is lit - tle don - key shay."

Verse 2:
Some says nasty things about the moke
One cove thinks 'is leg is really broke
That's 'is envy, cos we're carriage folk
Like the toffs as rides in Rotten Row!
Straight! It woke the alley up a bit
Thought our lodger would 'ave 'ad a fit
When my missus, who's a real wit
Says "I 'ates a Bus because it's low!"

Verse 3:
When we starts the blessed donkey stops
He won't move, so out I quickly 'ops
Pals start whackin' him, when down he drops
Someone says he wasn't made to go.
Lor it might 'ave been a four in 'and
My old Dutch knows 'ow to do the grand
First she bows, and then she waves 'er 'and
Calling out we're goin' for a blow!

Verse 4:
Ev'ry evenin' on the stroke of five
Me and missus takes a little drive
You'd say, "Wonderful they're still alive"
If you saw that little donkey go.
I soon showed him that 'e'd have to do
Just whatever he was wanted to
Still I shan't forget that rowdy crew,
'Ollerin' "Woa! steady! Neddy Woa!"

Music compiled by Peter Evans and Peter Lavender
Song background notes by Michael Kennedy

Text edited by Pearce Marchbank

Book design by Pearce Marchbank and Ben May
Text and image research by Katie Cornford

Printed in the United Kingdom by
Page Bros Ltd, Norwich, Norfolk

usive Distributors:
sic Sales Limited
Frith Street,
don W1V 5TZ, England.
sic Sales Pty Limited
Rothschild Avenue,
ebery, NSW 2018,
tralia.

er No. AM944163
10-7119-6598-6
book © Copyright 1998
Vise Publications

ur Guarantee of Quality
oublishers, we strive to produce every book
he highest commercial standards.
book has been carefully designed to minimise
ward page turns and to make playing from
real pleasure.
cicular care has been given to specifying acid-free,
tral-sized paper made from pulps which have not
n elemental chlorine bleached. This pulp is from
ned sustainable forests and was produced with
cial regard for the environment.
oughout, the printing and binding have been
ned to ensure a sturdy, attractive publication
ch should give years of enjoyment.
ur copy fails to meet our high standards,
ase inform us and we will gladly replace it.

sic Sales' complete catalogue describes thousands
itles and is available in full colour sections by
ject, direct from Music Sales Limited.
ase state your areas of interest and send a
que/postal order for £1.50 for postage to:
sic Sales Limited, Newmarket Road, Bury St.
nunds, Suffolk IP33 3YB.

t the Internet Music Shop at
p://www.musicsales.co.uk

Wise Publications
London/New York/Paris/Sydney/Copenhagen/Madrid

It is better to be making the
news than taking it; to be an
actor rather than a critic.
WINSTON CHURCHILL
(RIGHT) MATA HARI, EROTIC
DANCER AND GERMAN SPY,
EXECUTED 1917

'The unsinkable Titanic'.
ADVERTISEMENT, 1912.
(LEFT) THE TITANIC AND HER
SISTER SHIP THE OLYMPIC UNDER
CONSTRUCTION IN BELFAST IN 1910

Terminological inexactitude.
WINSTON CHURCHILL

I'm just going outside
and I may be some time.
CAPTAIN LAWRENCE OATES'
LAST WORDS ON SCOTT'S
ILL-FATED 1912 EXPEDITION
TO THE SOUTH POLE (RIGHT)

Nothing in life is so exhilirating in
life as to be shot at without result.
WINSTON CHURCHILL.
(ABOVE) ONE OF CHURCHILL'S
BEST-SELLING BOOKS OF THE 1910's

ou can tell the ideals of a
tion by it's advertisements.
ORMAN DOUGLAS, 1917.
CING PAGE) ENAMEL STREET
VERTISING SIGNS c.1910

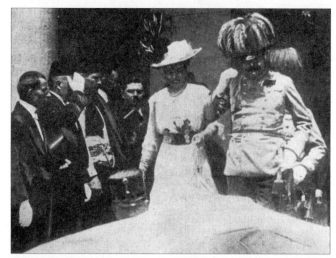

Assasination is the extreme form of censorship.

GEORGE BERNARD SHAW, IN 'MAN AND SUPERMAN', 1903. (LEFT) ARCHDUKE FERDINAND JUST BEFORE HIS ASSASINATION IN SARAJEVO, JUNE 1914: THE ACT THAT TRIGGERED THE FIRST WORLD WAR

I am not a criminal, for I destroyed a bad man. I thought it was right.

GAVRILO PRINCECIP, THE ASSASIN

The lamps are going out all over Europe; we shall not see them lit again in our lifetime.

EDWARD, VISCOUNT GREY, 1914 (ABOVE) A 1915 RECRUITING POSTER; CONSCRIPTION BECAME COMPULSORY THE NEXT YEAR

Armed neutrality is ineffectual enough at best... the world must be made safe for democracy.

WOODROW WILSON, 1917. (BELOW) THE PARIS PEACE CONFERENCE, 1919: LLOYD GEORGE OF ENGLAND, ORLANDO OF ITALY, CLEMENCEAU OF FRANCE AND WOODROW WILSON OF THE USA

If I should die think only this of me: that there's some corner of a foreign field that is forever England.

RUPERT BROOK IN 'THE SOLDIER', 1914

Who will remember, passing through this gate, the unheroic dead who fed the guns? Who shall absolve the foulness of their fate, those doomed, conscripted, unvictorious ones?

SIEGFRIED SASSOON IN 'ON PASSING THE NEW MENIN GATE', 1918 (RIGHT) THE MENIN ROAD, 1917

Peace is not only better than war but infinitely more arduous.

GEORGE BERNARD SHAW, 1918

"Votes for Women," November 26, 1915.   Registered at the G.P.O. as a Newspaper.

The War Paper for Women
VOTES FOR WOMEN

OFFICIAL ORGAN OF THE UNITED SUFFRAGISTS

VOL. IX. (Third Series), No. 403.   FRIDAY, NOVEMBER 26, 1915.   Price 1d. Weekly (Post Free 1½d.)

VOTES FOR HEROINES AS WELL AS HEROES

CHIVALRY

POLITICAL FREEDOM FOR WOMEN.

MORE VOTES FOR MEN

VOTES FOR HEROES

VOTES FOR SOLDIERS AND SAILORS

A PATRIOT

CHIVALRY: "Men and women protect one another in the hour of death. With the addition of the woman's vote, they would be able to protect one another in life as well."

VOGUE

GOOD HOUSEKEEPING

VOTES FOR WOMEN

Genius is one per cent
inspiration and ninety-nine
per cent perspiration!

THOMAS EDISON; INVENTOR OF
THE GRAMOPHONE (RIGHT), THE
ELECTRIC LIGHT, THE ELECTRIC
RAILWAY, MOTION PICTURES...
(ABOVE, LEFT) WITH HIS THREE
FAMOUS INVENTOR FRIENDS: FORD,
BURROUGHS AND FIRESTONE

Ah! Sweet Mystery Of Life

Music by Victor Herbert
Words by Rida Johnson Young

Irish born composer Victor Herbert found musical success in America. His operetta Naughty Marietta (1910), written with lyricist Rida Johnson Young, was set in New Orleans in 1780. The vivacious heroine Marietta promises to marry whoever can finish the melody of a certain song. That man is dashing Captain Richard, the song 'Ah! Sweet Mystery Of Life'.

hopes, the joy and i - dle tears that fall!_____ For 'tis love, and love a-lone, the world is

seek - ing; And 'tis love, and love a-lone, that can re - pay, 'tis the

ans - wer, 'tis the end and all of liv - ing,_____ for it is

love a - lone that rules for aye! For 'tis

love, and love a-one, the world is seek-ing, for 'tis love, and love a-lone, that can re-

-pay! 'tis the ans - wer, 'tis the end and all of

liv ing,____ for it is love a - lone that rules for aye!____

Any Old Iron

Music by Charles Collins
Words by Fred Terry & A. E. Sheppard

William Henry Crump was better known as top-of-the-bill music hall artiste Harry Champion who specialised in songs about food and drink. However, even he couldn't resist the 1911 showstopper 'Any Old Iron'. The song was resurrected for use during the Second World War to encourage the collection of scrap metal and railings.

1. Just a week or two a-go my poor old Un-cle Bill, *(Verses 2 - 4 see block lyric)* went and kick'd the buck-et and he left me in his will. The oth-er day I popp'd a-round to see poor Aun-tie Jane, she

said "Your Unc - le Bill has left to you a watch and chain." I put it on

right a - cross my vest, thought I look'd a dan - dy as it

dan - gled on my chest. Just to flash it off I start - ed

walk - ing round a - bout, a lot of kid - dies foll - ow'd me and all be - gan to shout:

"A - ny old iron, a - ny old iron, a - ny, a - ny old, old i - ron? You look neat, talk a - bout a treat, you look dap - per from your nap - per to your feet. Dress'd in style, brand new tile, and your fath - er's old green tie on, but I

12

would - n't give you tup - pence for your old watch chain, old i - ron, old i - ron?" i - ron?'

Verse 2:
I went to the City once and thought I'd have a spree
The Mayor of London, he was there, that's who I went to see
He dashed up in a canter, with a carriage and a pair
I shouted "Holler boys" and threw my hat up in the air.

Just then the Mayor he began to smile
Saw my face and then he shouted "Lummy what a dial!"
Started a Lord Mayoring and I thought that I should die
When pointing to my watch and chain he holler'd to me "Hi!"

Verse 3:
Just to have a little bit of fun the other day
Made up in my watch and chain I went and drew my pay
Then got out with a lot of other Colonels "on the loose"
I got full right up to here in fourp'ny "stagger juice."

One of them said "We want a pot of ale
"Run him to the ragshop, and we'll bung him on the scale"
I heard the fellow say "What's in this bundle that you've got"
Then whisper to me kindly: "Do you want to lose your lot?"

Verse 4:
Shan't forget when I got married to Selina Brown
The way the people laugh'd at me, it made me feel a clown
I began to wonder, when their dials began to crack
If by mistake I'd got my Sunday trousers front to back.

I wore my chain on my darby kell
The sun was shining on it and it made me look a swell
The organ started playing and the bells began to ring
My chain began to rattle, so the choir began to sing.

13

Alexander's Ragtime Band

Words & Music by Irving Berlin

First sung by Eddie Miller and Helen Vincent at the Garden Cafe in New York in 1911, 'Alexander's Ragtime Band' was an early hit for composer Irving Berlin. It was sung by Ethel Merman in the film of the same name - and Johnie Ray in There's No Business Like Show Business, *Britain first heard the song in the revue* Hello Ragtime, *which starred Lew Hearn and Shirley Kellogg.*

Moderato

1. Oh, ma hon - ey, oh, ma hon - ey, bet - ter hur - ry and
(Verse 2 see block lyric)

16

that's just the best-est band that am, hon-ey lamb; come on a-long,_____ come on a-long,_____ let me take you by the hand,_____ up to the man,_____ up to the man_____ who's the lead-er of the band,_____ and if you

Verse 2:
Oh, ma honey, oh, ma honey
There's a fiddle with notes that screeches
Like a chicken, like a chicken
And the clarinet, is a colored pet
Come and listen, come and listen
To a classical band what's peaches
Come now, some how
Better hurry along.

Blues My Naughty Sweetie Gives To Me

Words & Music by Arthur N. Swanstrom,
Charles R. McGarron & Carey Morgan

Although a prolific songwriter, Arthur Swanstrom's greatest and most enduring hit was 'Blues My Naughty Sweetie Gives To Me', written in cahoots with Charles R. McGarron and Carey Morgan. From its first appearance in 1919 it quickly became a jazz standard, memorably recorded by Jimmy Noone and Ted Lewis and his orchestra.

1. What is that song— a - bout kiss - es?— What is that song— a - bout

(Verse 2 see block lyric)

Chorus 2:

There are blues that you get when single
Those are blues that will give you pain
And there are blues when you're lonely
For your one and only
The blues you can never explain
There are blues that you get from longing
To hold someone on your knee
But the kind of blues that always stabs
Comes from hiring taxicabs
The blues my naughty sweetie gives to me.

Verse 2:

No use in chasing those rainbows
Rainbows will never help you
They look so bright and gay
But they will fade away
Then you'll find the sky's all blue
Look at the ocean and that's blue
My sweetie's eyes are blue too
When she got me she blew away
And natur'ly that makes me blue.

Chorus 3:

There are blues that you get from sweetie
When she 'phones to another guy
And there are blues when your honey
Spends all of your money
And blues when she tells you a lie
There are blues that you get when married
Wishing that you could be free
But the kind of blues that's good and blue
Comes from buying wine for two
The kind of blues my sweetie gives to me.

23

Don't Dilly Dally On The Way

Words & Music by Fred W. Leigh & Charles Collins

The composer of 'Any Old Iron', Charles Collins, combined with the lyricist of 'Waiting At The Church', Fred Leigh, to write in 1915 the definitive song about moving house which became a favourite of the queen of the music hall, Marie Lloyd. It is also known by its first line - 'My Old Man Said "Follow The Van"'.

had to move a-way, 'cos the rent we could-n't pay, the

(Verses 2 & 3 see block lyrics)

dal - ly on the way!" Off went the cart with the home packed in it, I walked be - hind with my old cock lin - net. But I dil - lied and dal - lied, dal - lied and dil - lied, lost the van and don't know where to roam.

1. I
2. Now
3. You

Verse 2:

I gave a helping hand with the marble wash-hand-stand,
And straight, we wasn't getting on so bad
All at once the carman bloke had an accident and broke
Well, the nicest bit of china that we had.

You'll understand of course, I was cross about the loss
Same as any other human woman would
But I soon got over that, what with "two-out" and a chat
'Cos it's little things like that what does you good.

Verse 3:

Oh! I'm in such a mess– I don't know the new address–
Don't even know the blessed neighbourhood
And I feel as if I might have to stay out all the night
And that ain't a-goin' to do me any good.

I don't make no complaint, but I'm coming over faint
What I want now is a good substantial feed
And I sort o' kind o' feel, if I don't soon have a meal
I shall have to rob the linnet of his seed.

I'll Take You Home Again Kathleen

Words & Music by Thomas P. Westendorf

Although it sounds like an authentic Irish ballad, 'I'll Take You Home Again Kathleen' was written in either Indiana or Kentucky (the composer moved around a lot) by Thomas P. Westendorf. He wrote the song to comfort his wife who wanted to return to the East Coast. Her name, incidentally, was Jennie!

1. I'll take you home again, Kath-
(Verses 2 & 3 see block lyrics)

-leen, a-cross the o-cean wild and wide, to

where your heart has ev-er been, since first you were my bon-ny bride. The ro - ses all have left your cheek, I've watched them fade a-way and die; your voice is sad when-e'er you speak, and tears be-dim your lov-ing eyes. Oh!

I will take you back, Kath - leen, to where your heart will feel no pain, and when the fields are fresh and green, I'll—— take you to your home a - gain.

Verse 2:
I know you love me, Kathleen dear
Your heart was ever fond and true
I always feel when you are near
That life holds nothing dear but you.

The smiles that once you gave to me
I scarcely ever see them now
Though many, many times I see
A dark'ning shadow on your brow.

Verse 3:
To that dear home beyond the sea
My Kathleen shall again return
And when thy old friends welcome thee
Thy loving heart will cease to yearn.

Where laughs the little silver stream
Beside your mother's humble cot
And brightest rays of sunshine gleam
There all your grief will be forgot.

Fred Murray wrote this splendidly unsubtle music hall success in 1910. It was both sung and recorded by Harry Champion, born in Shoreditch and always a full blooded performer, who specialised in singing his songs at terrific speed. He continued to perform right into his seventies.

Ginger, You're Balmy
Words & Music by Fred Murray

1. I'm al - ways in the fash - ion, I'm a not - ed chap for that, so
(Verses 2 & 3 see block lyric)

late - ly I've been walk - ing a - bout the streets with - out a hat. I do with - out a ca - dy, and it

saves me half a quid. I'm like a bloom - ing sauce - pan on the fire with-out a lid.

I go you know, strol - ling round the town, and wag my lit - tle cane a -

- bout. Girls they all say "Gin - ger's on the mash!" Then

dig me in the ribs and loud - ly shout,

"Don't walk a-bout with-out your ca-dy on; Gin - ger, you're balm - y! Get your hair cut!" they all be-gin to cry. "With noth - ing on your nap - per, oh, you are a pie! Pies must have a lit - tle bit of crust, why don't you join the ar - my? If you

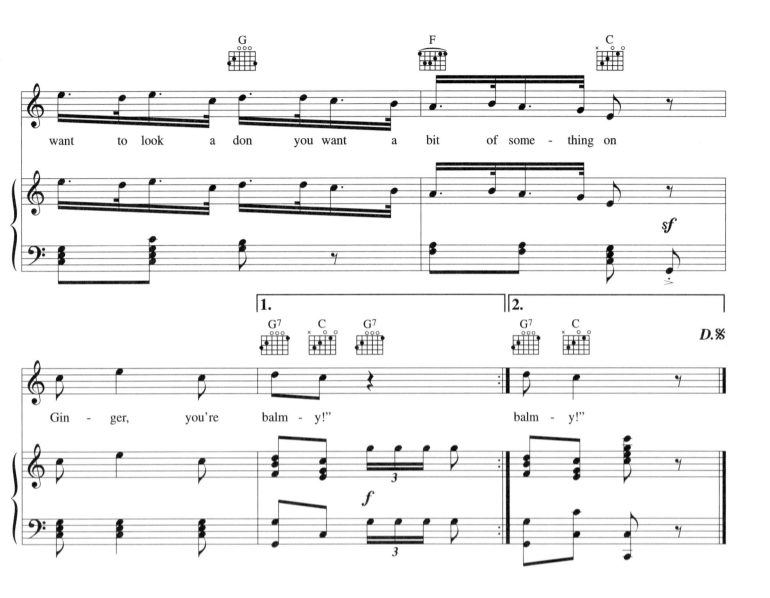

want to look a don you want a bit of some - thing on

1. Gin - ger, you're balm - y!"

2. balm - y!"

D.%

Verse 2:

One day I went into the zoo with such a smiling face
But, oh! there was a hullabaloo when I got in the place
The keeper started chasing me, though I was in a rage
They put a chain around my neck and bunged me in a cage.

I cried, "I'm not a monkey, on my word!"
Then I had to buy them all some beer
When they let me out they told me this
"If you want to keep away from here:"

Verse 3:

My missus took me in a pub; the guv'nor, Mister Hogg
He stroked my head and gave me a cake, he took me for a dog
A p'liceman stopped the traffic, shouted out with all his might
"Look out! here comes the North Pole with the top part all alight."

My wife said, "Your napper's like a sieve
"It's full of little holes I bet!
"When it rains 'twill let the water in
"And then your feet will both of 'em get wet."

American composer Nat D. Ayer came to
Britain with the American Ragtime Octette
in 1910 and stayed on to write a stream of
hits. In 1916 he wrote 'If You Were The Only
Girl In The World' for the London revue
The Bing Boys Are Here, starring Violet
Loraine. It has remained one of the most
beloved of all show songs.

If You Were The Only
Girl In The World

Music by Nat D. Ayer
Words by Clifford Grey

we could go on lov - ing in the same old way. A

Gar - den of E - den just made for two, with

noth - ing to mar our joy,

I would say such won - der - ful things to you,

Ped.

39

Lily Of Laguna

Words & Music by Leslie Stuart

*Leslie Stuart wrote his greatest success
for the blackface singer Eugene Stratton
(a precursor of Al Jolson) who first performed
'Lily Of Laguna' at the Oxford Music Hall in
1898. Laguna, according to its composer,
is on the road from New Orleans to California,
a hundred miles to the left. Errol Flynn sang
the ditty in Lilacs In The Spring.
The original lyrics to this song may be considered
racially insensitive; however, they have been
included for historical authenticity.*

1. It's de same old tale of a pal- pa-ta- ting nig- gar ev- 'ry
(Verse 2 see block lyric)

time, ev- 'ry time; it's de same old

Verse 2:

When I first met Lil it was down in old Laguna at de dance, oder night
So she says, "Say, a'm curious for to know
"When ye leave here de way yer goin' to go
"'Kase a wants to see who de lady is dat claims ye all way home, way home tonight."

I says, "I've no gal, never had one,"
And den ma Lilly, ma Lilly, ma Lilly gal!
She says, kern't believe ye, a kern't believe ye
Else I'd like to have ye shapperoon me.

Dad says he'll esscortch me, says he'll esscortch me
But it's mighty easy for to lose him"
Since then each sun down I wander down here and roam around
Until I know ma lady wants me
Till I hear de music ob de signal sound.

MacNamara's Band

Words by John J. Stamford
Music by Shamus O'Connor

This optimistic 1917 song, full of bravado, by John J. Stamford and Shamus O'Connor, has long been a favourite. It featured in two films: I'll Get By, which starred Dennis Day, a singer who made a speciality of 'Irish' songs, and Bad Lands Of Dakota, a Western with Robert Stack and Ann Rutherford.

1. My name is Mac-na-ma-ra, I'm the lead-er of the band, and tho' we're small in num-ber we're the best in all the land! Oh!

I am the con-duc-tor and we oft-en have to play with all the best mu-

rit.   a tempo

-si-cian-ers you hear a-bout to-day, when the drums go bang, the cym-bals clang, the

horns will blaze a - way,— Mac-Car-thy puffs the ould bas-soon while Doyle the pipes will

play; Oh! Hen-nes-sy Ten-nes-sy too-tles the flute, my word! 'tis some-thing grand, Oh! a

2. When - ev - er an e -
(Verse 3 see block lyric)

- lec - tion's on we play on ei - ther side.＿＿ The way we play our

fine ould airs fills Ir - ish hearts with pride, oh! if poor Tom Moore was

liv - ing now, he'd make yez un - der - stand＿＿＿ that none could do him

49

la   la,_____ tra-la-la   la   la,   tra-la-la   la   la   la   la   la la   la

la,   tra-la-la   la   la,_____   tra-la-la   la   la,   tra-la-

1.
la   la   la   la   la   la   la   la   la,   tra-la-la la!   la,   tra-la-la la!
2.

Verse 3:
We play at wakes and weddings, and at ev'ry county ball
And at any great man's funeral we play the "Dead March in Saul"
When the Prince of Wales to Ireland came, he shook me by the hand
And said he'd never heard the like of "Macnamara's band."

Originally written in 1912, with lyrics added a year later, 'Memphis Blues' was the work of the so called 'father of the blues' William Christopher Handy and was used during the political campaign of a Memphis politician, William H. Crump. The song was featured in the films St Louis Blues (a biography of its composer) and Birth Of The Blues. The original lyrics to this song may be considered racially insensitive; however, they have been included for historical authenticity.

Memphis Blues

Words & Music by W. C. Handy

1. Hon - ey I've__ been down, down to Mem - phis town, where the peo - ple smile
(Verse 2 see block lyric)

on you all__ the while; hos - pi - ta - li - ty, they were good__ to me,

could-n't spend— a dime, had the grand-est time, I went out a-dance-in' with a
Ten-nes-see dear,— a fel-low there nam'd Han-dy had a band you should hear,—
while they gent-ly swayed, all them dark-ies played real_____ har-mon-
-y._____ I nev-er will for-get__ the tune that Han-dy called the Mem-phis

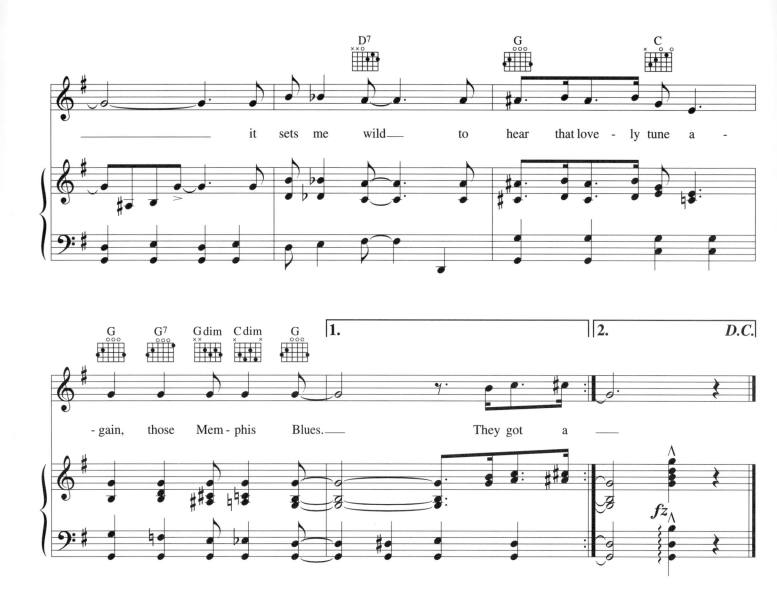

Verse 2:
Oh, that melody sure appeals to me
Like a mountain stream, flowing on it seem'd
Then it slowly died, with a gentle sigh
As the breeze that whines in the summer pines
Hear me people, hear me people, hear me, I pray
I'll take a million lessons till I learn how to play
Seems I hear it yet, simply can't forget, that blue refrain
There's nothing like the Handy Band
That plays the Memphis Blues so grand, oh them blues.

Moonlight Bay

Music by Percy Wenrich
Words by Edward Madden

Percy Wenrich from Joplin, Massachusetts started by playing in saloons and bars and sold his own self published compositions door-to-door. He subsequently wrote for many Broadway shows and married singer Dolly Connolly. He was 32 when he wrote one of his big hits 'Moonlight Bay', sung by Alice Faye in Tin Pan Alley and Doris Day in a film named for the song.

moon - beams play._____ All a - lone____ un - known

_____ they find me, mem - o - ries_____ like these_____ re - mind me

of the girl____ I left____ be - hind me, down on Moon - light Bay. We were sail - ing a -

- long_____ on Moon-light Bay,_____ we could hear the voi - ces

Verse 2:
Candle lights gleaming on the silent shore
Lonely nights, dreaming till we meet once more.
Far apart, her heart is yearning
With a sigh for my returning
With the light of love still burning
As in days of yore.

Oh! You Beautiful Doll

Words & Music by Seymour Brown & Nat D. Ayer

An early (1911) hit for American born Nat D. Ayer was 'Oh! You Beautiful Doll', which he wrote before coming to Britain, in partnership with A. Seymour Brown. It became the melody of car horns in the 1920s, was the title tune of a 40s film and was danced to by Fred Astaire and Ginger Rogers in the biographical film The Story Of Vernon And Irene Castle.

Moderato

1. Hon-ey dear,— want you near,— just turn out the light and then come
(Verse 2 see block lyric)

ov-er here;— nes-tle close____ up to my side,—

my heart's _____ a - fire _____ with love's de - sire. _____

_____ In my arms _____ rest com - plete, _____ I

nev - er thought that life could ev - er be so sweet _____ till I met you _____

_____ some time a - go, _____ but now _____ you know _____

Lyrics:

I love you so.

Oh! you beau-ti-ful doll, you great big beau-ti-ful doll!

Let me put my arms a-bout you, I could nev-er live with-out you,

Oh! you beau-ti-ful doll, you great big beau-ti-ful doll! If you

Verse 2:
Precious prize, close your eyes
Now we're goin' to visit lover's paradise
Press your lips again to mine
For love is king of ev'rything.

Squeeze me, dear, I don't care!
Hug me just as if you were a grizzly bear
This is how I'll go thro' life
No care or strife when you're my wife.

Your King And Country Want You

Words & Music by Paul A. Rubens

1. We've watched you play-ing cric-ket and ev-'ry kind of game at
(Verses 2 & 3 see block lyric)

foot-ball, golf and po-lo, you men have made your name, but now your coun-try calls you to

* When used for Male Voice substitue the word "bless" for kiss.

Chord diagrams and melody line:
C¹¹ C⁷   F   D⁷   G

want you   and miss you   but with all our might and main   we shall

C   A⁷   F   *a tempo*   Dm⁷ G⁷   C

cheer you, thank you, *kiss you, when you come back   a - gain.

last verse

a tempo

last time colla voce

D.C.

Verse 2:
We want you from all quarters
So, help us, South and North
We want you in your thousands
From Falmouth to the Forth
You'll never find us fail you
When you are in distress
So, answer when we hail you
And let your word be "yes"
And so your name, in, years to come
Each mother's son shall bless.

Encore Verse
It's easy for us women/people
To stay at home and home and shout
But remember, there's a duty
To the men who *first* went out
The odds against that handful
Were nearly four to one
And we cannot rest until
It's man for man, and gun for gun!
And ev'ry woman's/body's duty
Is to see that duty done!

* When used for Male Voices substitute the word "bless" for kiss.

Why Am I Always The Bridesmaid?

Words & Music by Charles Collins & Fred W. Leigh

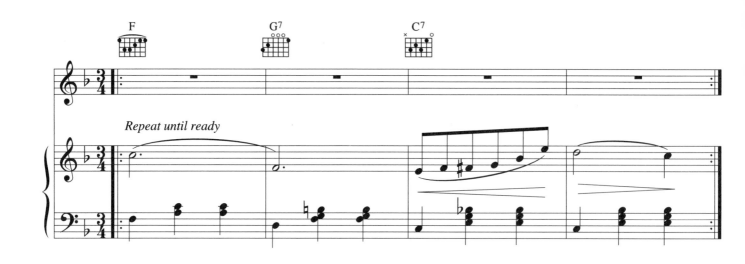

1. Why am I dressed in these beau-ti-ful clothes?
(Verses 2 & 3 see block lyrics)

What is the mat-ter with me?

I've been the brides - maid for twen - ty - two brides,

this time - 'll make twen - ty - three.

Twen - ty - two la - dies I've helped off the shelf,

no doubt it seemd a bit strange.

being the brides-maid is no good to me, and I

think I could do with a change.

Why am I al-ways the brides - - - maid, nev-er the

blush-ing bride?_____ Ding - - dong!

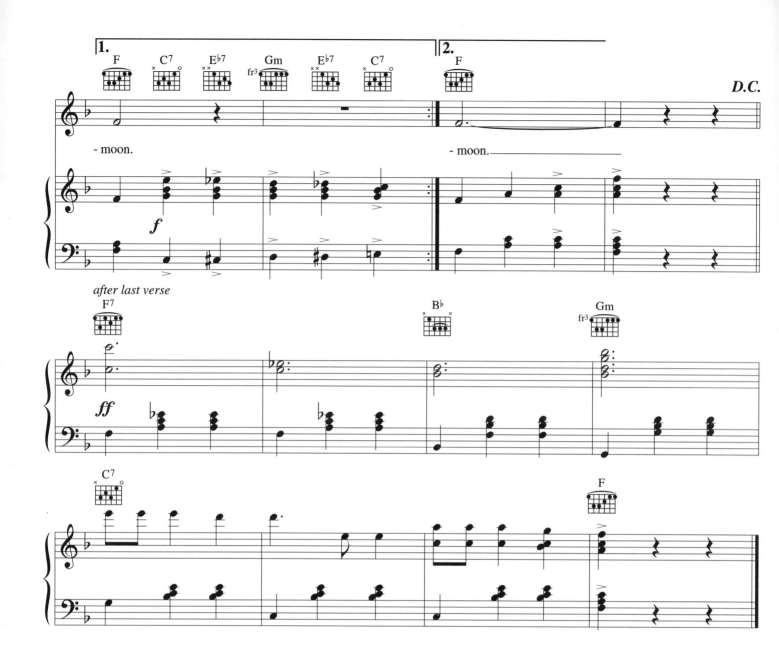

Verse 2:
Twenty-two times have I gone to the church
Followed the bride up the aisle
Twenty-two ladies have answered "I will"
Meaning "I won't" all the while.

Twenty-two couples I've seen go away
Just him and her on their own
Twenty-two times I have wished it was me
And gone back home to Mother alone.

Verse 3:
I had a good chance a week or two back
Took my young man home to tea
Mother got playful and gave him a pinch
Pinched my "financy" from me.

Being a widow she knew what to do
No use for me to complain
When they got married today, if you please
I was only the bridesmaid again.

Music for the Millennium **The Twenties**

Music compiled by Peter Evans and Peter Lavender
Song background notes by Michael Kennedy

All text photographs courtesy of Hulton Getty

Cover photograph of Louise Brooks
from The Kobal Collection

Edited by Pearce Marchbank

Text researched and compiled by Heather Page
Book design by Pearce Marchbank and Ben May
Picture research by Nikki Russell

Printed in the United Kingdom by
Page Bros Ltd, Norwich, Norfolk

...usive Distributors:
...ic Sales Limited
...rith Street,
...on W1V 5TZ, England.
...Rothschild Avenue,
...ebery, NSW 2018,
...ralia.

...er No. AM92355
...0-7119-4431-8
... book © Copyright 1997
...Wise Publications

Wise Publications
London/New York/Paris/Sydney/Copenhagen/Madrid

Any lover of the beautiful
will die rather than be
associated with the
Charleston. It is neurotic!
It is rotten! It stinks!
Phew, open the windows!
VICAR OF ST AIDAN'S, BRISTOL

The public are asking for filth
…the younger generation
are knocking at the door
of the dustbin.
SIR GERALD DU MAURIER ON
NOEL COWARD'S 'THE VORTEX'

Modern popular music is more
barbarous than any folk art has
been for hundreds of years.
ALDOUS HUXLEY

Art Deco is the ultimate test
of tolerance thresholds.
BEVIS HILLIER

The Jazz Age was wicked
and monstrous and silly…
I had a good time.
HEYWOOD BROUN

The Twenties contained co-
educationists, Morris Dancers,
vegetarians, teetotallers, professors
of economics, drugtakers, boozers,
Socialists, gossip columnists,
playwrights, Communists, Roman
Catholic converts, painters and
poets having an uninhibited fling…
'psychological compensation'
for the years that preceded them.
DOUGLAS GOLDRING

Feast your weary optics up
this super-flapper of them a
refined, washed, manicur
pedicured, permanent-wav
and exalt
'VANITY FAIR' ON THE 'IT' (

'Don't eat between meals
...smoke a Kensitas instead.'
CIGARETTE ADVERTISEMENT

Advertising was the new giant
loudspeaker...the full-throated,
blaring horn telling millions
what to eat, what to drink
and what to wear.
WOLCOTT GIBBS IN
'THE NEW YORKER'

You will be a queen
when you grow up.
A GARDEN-PARTY PALMIST
TO THE TEN-YEAR-OLD
ELIZABETH BOWES-LYON

Hats off to the indestructible
Dancing Drinking Tumbling
Kissing Walking Talking and
Sleeping - but not Marrying -
idol of the British Empire!
'VANITY FAIR' ON THE PRINCE
OF WALES' VISIT TO AMERICA

'I've danced with a man,
Who's danced with a girl,
Who's danced with the
Prince of Wales.'

Before the Prince landed, the
popular idea of princes was of
something haughty and remote;
but this smiling, appealing
youthful man smoothed away
the difference which Australians
believed lay between Royalty
and the common people.
THE SYDNEY 'SUN' ON THE
VISIT OF THE PRINCE OF WALES

as TT until prohibition.
UCHO MARX

e cocktail is intended to
like unto a bugle call to
als. One cocktail helps,
do not, and three harm
flow of gastric juices.
RE SIMON

motion of the ship
cludes carrying the
er red wines.
UITANIA' FIRST-CLASS MENU

I don't want any more
skinny-legged women
in this paper...
I want women with
hips and breasts.
BERNARD MACFADDEN
IN THE NEW YORK
'EVENING GRAPHIC'

Larger-than-life ladies...
with short tubular dresses,
cigarettes with long holders,
cloche hats, bobbed hair,
plucked eyebrows, bands of
diamond bracelets from wrist
to elbow, and earrings hanging
like fuchsias... an utter
revolution in the concept of
femininity... more than
superficially related to
cubism in art.
CECIL BEATON IN
'THE GLASS OF FASHION'

I like them fluffy, I freely
confess, with fluffy blue eyes
and a fluffy blue dress,
and fluffy fair hair, and
no brains at all.
A.P. HERBERT ON BLONDES
IN 'PUNCH'

No corsets, bad money
and general moral laxity.
JAMES LAVER,
FASHION HISTORIAN

The American woma
has lifted her skirts far bey
any modest limitat
'NEW YORK TIMES' FASHION ED

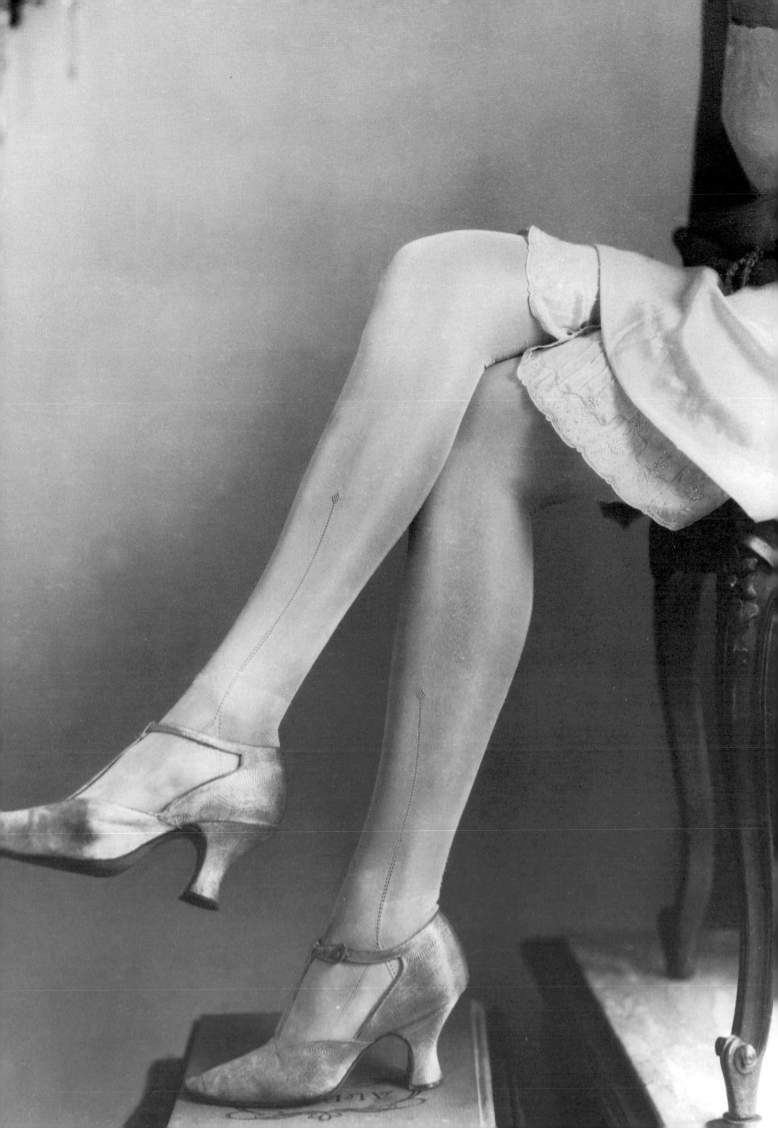

'Where am I?'
'Paris.'
'I've been to eternity and back.
I know how the dead would
feel to live again.'
CHARLES. LINDBERGH ON
CROSSING THE ATLANTIC IN
HIS PLANE 'SPIRIT OF ST LOUIS'

Michelangelo would have
fainted for joy with the
beauty of his profile, which
is almost pure Greek.
A FEMALE REPORTER FOR THE
NEW YORK 'EVENING WORLD'
ON JACK DEMPSEY, THE BOXER

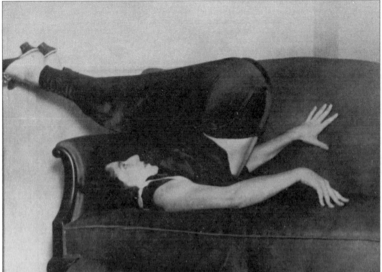

She has high spirits, but
there's no harm in that.
SENATOR BANKHEAD ON HIS
DAUGHTER TALLULAH'S
OUTRAGEOUS BEHAVIOUR

one for tennis?
NILE LEAD IN ENGLISH LIGHT COMEDY

nne is playing today…
ss my mah-jong party is sunk.
TY HOSTESS ON SUZANNE LENGLEN,
CH TENNIS STAR

You had to stand in line to
get a window to jump out of.
WILL ROGERS ON THE WALL STREET CRASH

The driver of this bus is a student
of Guy's Hospital. The conductor
is a student of Guy's. Anyone who
interferes with either is liable
to be a patient of Guy's.
VOLUNTEER DURING THE GENERAL STRIKE, 1926

The main cause of its peaceful defeat
was that the public was with the
government, but without resentment
against the strikers, while the mass of
strikers themselves struck out of
loyalty to the movement rather
than from any passionate conviction
of the justice of their cause.
L S AMERY ON THE GENERAL STRIKE OF 1926

Baby Won't You Please Come Home

Words & Music by Charles Warfield & Clarence Williams.

A perennial favourite with jazz singers, this song was written by lyricist Charles Warfield in 1919 with the youthful Clarence Williams, composer of 'Royal Garden Blues'. The latter was a pianist, arranger, publisher and bandleader, married to noted jazz/blues singer Eva Taylor. Even an accident with a taxi in 1956, which blinded him, did not stop Williams from composing.

Medium bounce tempo

I've got the blues, I feel so lone - ly, I'd give the world if I could on - ly make you un - der - stand. It sure - ly would be grand. I'm goin' to tel - e - graph you ba - by,

Show Me The Way To Go Home

Words & Music by Irving King.

Irving King is remembered today for just one song - 'Show Me The Way To Go Home', made famous in the early years of the century by male impersonator Ella Shields. The song has come to be associated with gentlemen who have drunk not wisely but too well. There are memorable recorded versions, by Michael Holliday and The Andrews Sisters.

Moderately

When I'm hap-py, when I'm hap-py, sing-ing all the
Old king Cole was a mer-ry old soul, and a mer-ry old soul was

while, he, he I call'd don't for his need wine no-bo-dy and he then call'd to for his pipe and he

show me how to smile. When I've been out
call'd for his fid-dlers three. When they'd had a

on the spree, todd - ling down the street,
high old time, all the whole night thro'

With this lit - tle me - lo - dy eve - ry - one I
What was it that King Cole said and his fidd - lers

CHORUS

greet.
too?

Show me the way to go home, I'm

tired and I want to go to bed. I had a lit - tle drink a - bout an

hour a - go, and it's gone right to my head. Where

ev - er I may roam, on land, or sea, or

foam, you can al - ways hear me sing - ing this song,

show me the way to go home. home.

Amapola

Words by Albert Gamse. Music by Joseph M. Lacalle.

Deanna Durbin enjoyed her first screen kiss in First Love, a 1939 film which featured the 19-year-old Robert Stack whose pleasant task it was to proffer his affection. One of the hit songs was 'Amapola' by Joseph M. Lacalle and Albert Gamse that dated from 1924. The film made it a hit, thanks to both Jimmy Dorsey - and to Deanna Durbin herself.

poppy must copy its endearing charm from you. Amapola, Amapola, how I long to hear you say I love you. Amapola, love you.

Drifting And Dreaming
(Sweet Paradise)

Words by Haven Gillespie. Music by Egbert Van Alstyne,
Erwin R. Schmidt & Loyal Curtis.

Lyricist Haven Gillespie and composer Egbert Van Alstyne were responsible for many hits. Gillespie wrote 'Santa Claus Is Coming To Town', and 'Breezin' Along With The Breeze'. Van Alstyne composed 'In The Shade Of The Old Apple Tree' and 'Memories'. Together they co-wrote 'Drifting And Dreaming' in 1925. The song has been recorded by Vera Lynn, Bing Crosby and Nelson Riddle.

hear you call._____ Love's old sweet

sto - - - ry, told with your eyes,_____

drift - - - ing and dream - ing, sweet pa - ra -

dise._____

dise._____

D.%.al Fine
Fine

Baby Face

Words & Music by Harry Akst & Benny Davis.

Harry Akst scored a major hit with 'Baby Face', written in 1926 with Benny Davis and taken up by Al Jolson, who sang it in his second film biography, Jolson Sings Again, in 1949. In 1929 the song had cropped up in a part-Technicolor musical Glorifying The American Girl. In 1967 Julie Andrews sang it in the film musical Thoroughly Modern Millie

Ros - y cheeks and turn'd up nose and curl - y hair, _____ I'm rav - ing

'bout my ba - by now, _____ Pret - ty lit - tle dim - ples here and

dim - ples there; _____ Don't want to live with - out her, I love her good - ness

24

25

Can't Help Lovin' Dat Man

Music by Jerome Kern. Words by Oscar Hammerstein II.

'Can't Help Lovin' Dat Man' is just one of many hits from the musical score Show Boat, by Jerome Kern and Oscar Hammerstein II. It appeared in film versions of the show, as well as in Till The Clouds Roll By with Lena Horne as Julie Laverne, who knows that her love for Steve, her man, is far from perfect.

When he goes a - way dat's a rain - y

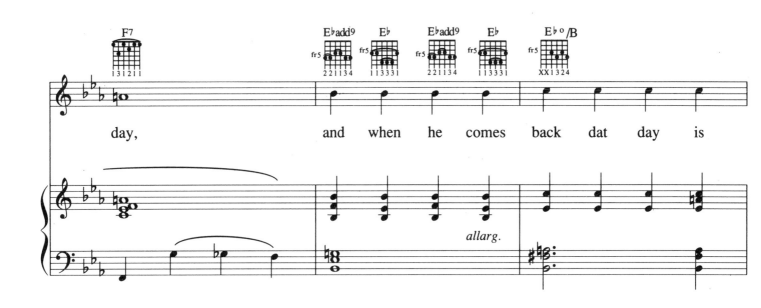

day, and when he comes back dat day is

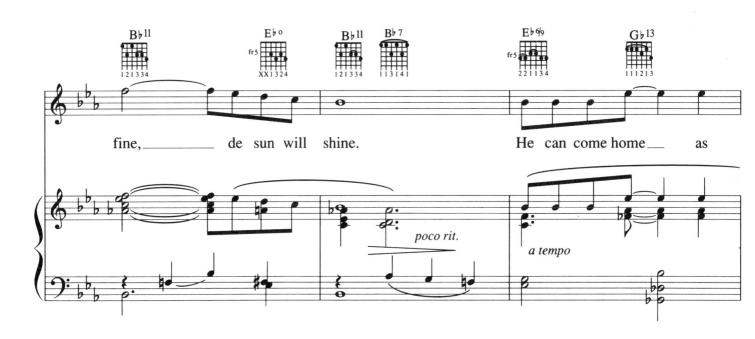

fine,_____ de sun will shine. He can come home____ as

late as can be,___ home wid-out him___ ain't no home to me,___

Can't help lov-in' dat man___ of mine.

mine.___

The Lonesome Road

Words by Gene Austin. Music by Nathaniel Shilkret.

horn._____
fore._____

Wea - ry to - tin' such a load, tredg - ing down that lone - some road. Look down, look down that lone - some road—— be - fore you tra - vel

1. on._____ True on._____ **2.**

31

Ol' Man River

Music by Jerome Kern. Words by Oscar Hammerstein II.

One of the principal characters of the stage musical and film Show Boat is the Mississippi River, celebrated by Joe, played by Jules Bledsoe on Broadway and Paul Robeson in London - and on film. This 1927 song runs like a ribbon through the show and gave Jerome Kern and Oscar Hammerstein II one of their biggest hits, and Paul Robeson his signature tune.

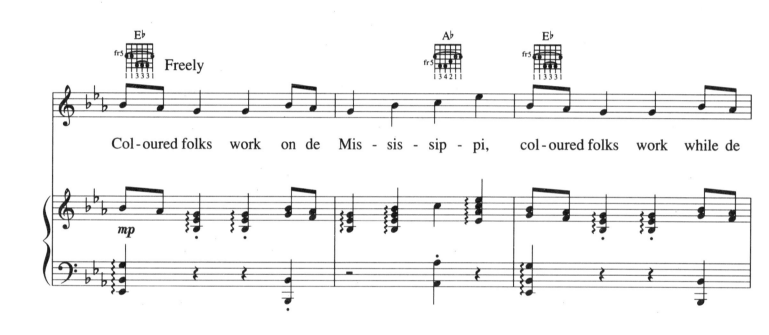

Col-oured folks work on de Mis-sis-sip-pi, col-oured folks work while de

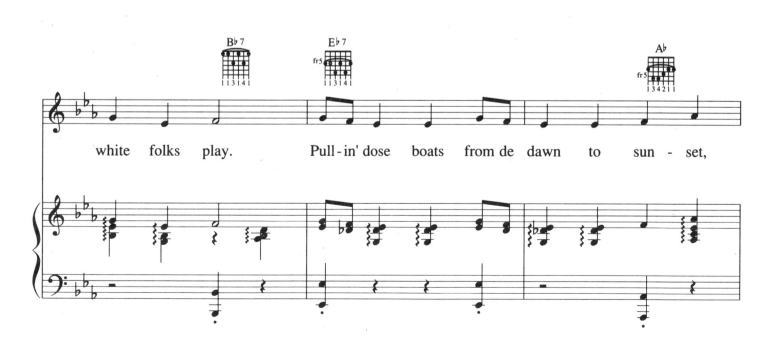

white folks play. Pull-in' dose boats from de dawn to sun-set,

git - tin' no rest till de judge - ment day. Don't look up 'an

don't look down, you don't dast make de white boss frown; Bend yo' knees an'

bow yo' head, an' pull dat rope un - til you're dead. Let me go 'way from de

piu mosso
mf

rall.

a tempo

jus' keeps roll-in' a - long._____ You 'an me, we

sweat and strain, Bo - dy all ach - in' an' racked wid pain. "Tote dat barge!"

"Lift dat bale," Git a lit - tle drunk an' you land in jail. Ah gits wea - ry an'

sick of try-in', Ah'm tired of liv-in' an' skeered of dy-in', but

ol' man riv-er, he jus' keeps roll-in' a - long.

long.

A Garden In The Rain

Words by James Dyrenforth. Music by Carroll Gibbons.

American pianist and bandleader *Carroll Gibbons made his home in Britain; and for decades led the dance band at the Savoy Hotel, London.*
He was also a fine composer: with James Dyrenforth he wrote 'A Garden In The Rain'- first a hit for George Metaxa in 1928. Years later, Perry Como, The Four Aces and Connie Francis revived the song.

VERSE

I re-call a sum-mer's day, When you and I had strolled a-way, And
I re-call our sud-den gasp, of pure de-light and then the clasp, of

sud-den-ly a storm drew nigh.___
hands that said, "Do you see too?"___

39

Sweet Sue - Just You

Words by Will J. Harris. Music by Victor Young.

Victor Young found his true métier in the 40s and 50s writing superb film scores in Hollywood, but in 1928 he was busy writing for the hit parade. 'Sweet Sue - Just You', co-written with the relatively obscure Will J. Harris, was featured in the film Rhythm Parade (1942) and sung by the great Omale close harmony group, The Mills Brothers.

43

I Can't Give You Anything But Love

Words by Dorothy Fields
Music by Jimmy McHugh

The Broadway revue Blackbirds Of 1928 introduced one of the greatest of love songs, written by veteran composer Jimmy McHugh with one of the century's great lyricists, Dorothy Fields. She would go on to write classic songs with Jerome Kern, Arthur Schwartz and Cy Coleman. But it was 'I Can't Give You Anything But Love (baby)' that first revealed her fully formed talent.

Moderately

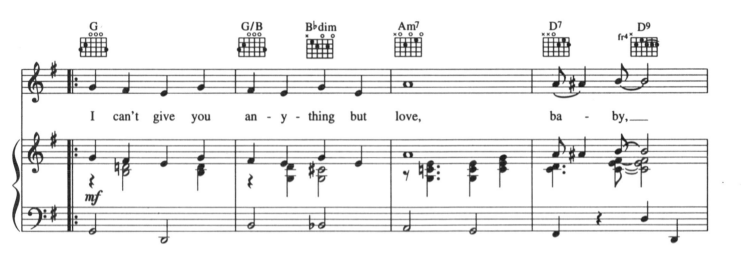

I can't give you an-y-thing but love, ba - by, ___

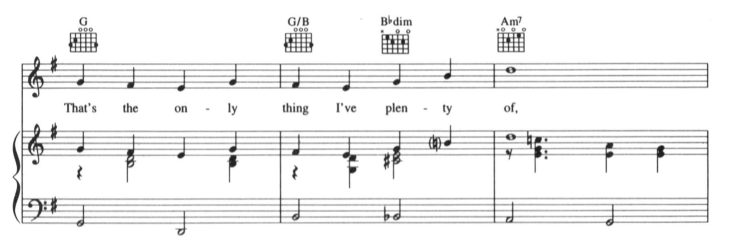

That's the on-ly thing I've plen-ty of,

46

Together

Buddy De Sylva, Lew Brown and Ray Henderson wrote many hits as a trio before De Sylva became a Hollywood producer. Their 1928 hit 'Together' was not written for any show, but was included in the biographical movies The Best Things In Life Are Free *and* Since You Went Away. *It was, however, sung on Broadway in* Good News, *in 1974, by Alice Faye.*

Words & Music by B.G. De Sylva, Lew Brown & Ray Henderson.

Moderately Slow

We strolled the lane, To-geth-er

Laughed at the rain, To-geth-er

Sang love's re-frain, To-geth-er. And we'd / We knew

49

That's My Weakness Now

Words & Music by Bud Green & Sam H. Stept.

Dream Lover

Words by Clifford Grey. Music by Victor Schertzinger.

The Love Parade, *a very early film operetta (1929) starring Jeanette MacDonald and Maurice Chevalier, was set in a mythical kingdom in central Europe among Princes and Princesses.* 'Dream Lover', *with words by Clifford Grey and music by Victor Schertzinger, was an instant success. Schertzinger went on to a successful career as a director.*

There's a land of charm that I know,
land of sweet ro-mance where I love to go;
And its

In the land where dreams ne-ver end,
Pa-ra-dise where bro-ken hearts quick-ly mend;
We will

52

bounds touch my room in the gloom, when the sha-dows creep.
wan-der en-rap-tured and whis-per sweet vows of love.

Some-one I met there waits for me, some-one
Not a cloud to there dark-en our sky, not a

ten-der as a lov-er should be; And I whis-per each night as I
care we'll ev-er know, you and I; All the days will be fair with the

close my eyes in sleep. Dream
sun a-shine a-bove.

Valse lente
CHORUS

53

lov - er fold your arms a - round me, dream

lov - er your ro - mance has found me, I'm

held in your spell, know - ing too well,

dreams nev - er tell. We

54

two can leave the world be - hind us, no - - -

bo - dy in - dis - creet can find us, dream

lov - er of mine, se - crets di - vine, I am

shar - ing with you. you.

Honeysuckle Rose

Music by Thomas 'Fats' Waller. Words by Andy Razaf.

Thomas 'Fats' Waller was a larger-than-life entertainer, whose jolly, ebullient personality is immediately apparent from his songs, his piano playing and his singing. 'Honeysuckle Rose' was written with lyricist Andy Razaf and first published in 1929. There have been renowned performances from Coleman Hawkins, and from Lena Horne in the film Thousands Cheer.

If I Had You

Words & Music by Ted Shapiro, Jimmy Campbell & Reg Connelly.

Ted Shapiro was Sophie Tucker's long-time accompanist, and wrote songs including 'If I Had You' (1929). His co-writers were the British publishing legends James Campbell and Reginald Connelly. Years later the song resurfaced in You Were Meant For Me, starring Jeanne Crain and Dan Dailey (1948) and also The Clock (1945) which starred Judy Garland.

glad all of the while I could change the grey skies to blue If I had

you._____ I could leave the old days be - hind, Leave all my

pals, I'd nev - er mind, I could start my life all a -

new If I had you._____ I could climb the snow capp'd

59

I'll Always Be In Love With You

Words & Music by Herman Ruby, Bud Green & Sam Stept.

Herman (Harry) Ruby, Bud Green and Sam Stept wrote 'I'll Always Be In Love With You' in 1929. Two films included the song, Steppin' High and Syncopation. The latter featured Fred Waring, who recorded the song - as did Vera Lynn and Michael Holliday.

rain._____ And tho' all my glad-ness has turn'd in-to sad-ness. Sweet-

CHORUS

heart if you should stray a mil-lion miles a-way, I'll al-ways be in love with

you,_____ and tho' you find more bliss in some-one el-ses kiss, I'll

al-ways be in love with you._____ I can't do a-ny-more, I've

Additional Verse (optional)
Sometimes when I'm all alone,
I keep wondering who is romancing with you.
How could I ever have known
I'd be broken hearted,
And now that we're parted.

(CHORUS)

Miss You

Words by Charlie Tobias & Harry Tobias. Music by Henry M. Tobias.

The brothers Tobias (Henry, Harry and Charles) were songwriters with a stream of hits. Their 1929 hit 'Miss You' turned out to be perennially popular. Apart from featuring in the obscure 'B' picture Strictly In The Groove (1942), it brought a deserved Top Twenty entry for disc jockey and erstwhile crooner Jimmy Young in the autumn of 1963.

that I still love you. Kiss you,

in my dreams I kiss you, Whis - p'ring,

"Dar-ling how I Miss You," Tell me,

do you ev - er miss me as I

Miss You. I You.

More Than You Know

*From the stage show Great Day (1929)
came 'More Than You Know', written by
Vincent Youmans and Edward Eliscu
(with showman/impresario Billy Rose).
The song, a hit for Helen Morgan, was
featured in the film Hit The Deck and in
the second Barbra Streisand film about
Fanny Brice, Funny Lady (1975).*

Words by William Rose & Edward Eliscu.
Music by Vincent Youmans.

67

68

Louise

Words by Leo Robin. Music by Richard A. Whiting.

Since he introduced the song in the 1929 film hit Innocents Of Paris, 'Louise' became the theme song of international film star Maurice Chevalier. It was written by Richard Whiting, father of popular singer Margaret Whiting, with celebrated lyricist Leo Robin. The film has long since vanished, but the song lives on.

Won - der - ful! Oh, it's won - der - ful, to be in love with you.
In - no - cent! You're as in - no - cent, and gen - tle as a dove.

Beau - ti - ful! You're so beau - ti - ful, you haunt me all day through.
Hea - ven sent! You were hea - ven sent, an an - gel from a - bove.

Ev - 'ry lit - tle breeze seems to whis - per "Lou - ise." — Birds in the trees — seem to

70

Music compiled by Peter Evans and Peter Lavender
Song background notes by Michael Kennedy

All text photographs courtesy of Hulton Getty

Cover photograph of Greta Garbo
from The Kobal Collection

Edited by Pearce Marchbank

Text researched and compiled by Heather Page
Book design by Pearce Marchbank and Ben May
Picture research by Nicki Russell

Printed in the United Kingdom by
Page Bros Ltd, Norwich, Norfolk

...usive Distributors:
...ic Sales Limited
...Frith Street,
...don W1V 5TZ, England.
...ic Sales Pty Limited
...Rothschild Avenue,
...ebery, NSW 2018,
...ralia.

...er No. AM92356
...0-7119-4432-6
...book © Copyright 1997
...Wise Publications

...ur Guarantee of Quality
...ublishers, we strive to produce every book
...he highest commercial standards.
...s book has been carefully designed to minimise
...ward page turns and to make playing from
...real pleasure.
...icular care has been given to specifying acid-free,
...tral-sized paper made from pulps which have not
...n elemental chlorine bleached. This pulp is from
...ed sustainable forests and was produced with
...cial regard for the environment.
...oughout, the printing and binding have been
...ned to ensure a sturdy, attractive publication
...ch should give years of enjoyment.
...ur copy fails to meet our high standards,
...se inform us and we will gladly replace it.

...ic Sales' complete catalogue describes thousands
...tles and is available in full colour sections by
...ect, direct from Music Sales Limited.
...se state your areas of interest and send a
...que/postal order for £1.50 for postage to:
...ic Sales Limited, Newmarket Road, Bury St.
...unds, Suffolk IP33 3YB.

...the Internet Music Shop at
...p://www.musicsales.co.uk

Wise Publications
London/New York/Paris/Sydney/Copenhagen/Madrid

Roll up your carpet and
dance at home to the finest
dance band in London.
BBC BROADCAST FROM
THE SAVOY HOTEL FEATURING
THE SAVOY ORPHEANS

How potent
cheap music is.
FROM 'PRIVATE LIVES'
BY NOEL COWARD

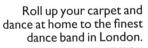

There is something
depressing about the way
in which a tram lumbers
and grinds along like a
sick elephant.
J B PRIESTLEY

Write to us about your
woes, whatever they are.
'WOMAN' MAGAZINE'S
ADVICE COLUMN

s Quicker by Rail.
VERTISEMENT FOR LNER

op Me and Buy One.
OGAN ON WALLS' ICE-CREAM BICYCLES

Filling stations and factories that look like exhibition buildings... giant cinemas and dance-halls and cafés, bungalows with tiny garages, cocktail bars, Woolworths, motor coaches, wireless, hiking, factory girls looking like actresses, greyhound racing and dirt tracks, swimming pools and everything given away for cigarette coupons.
J B PRIESTLEY ON THE NEW ENGLAND IN HIS BOOK 'ENGLISH JOURNEY'

There will be no war this year... or next.
'DAILY EXPRESS', 1939

England is a land of snobbery and privilege, ruled largely by the old and the silly.
GEORGE ORWELL, 1931

I have taken a fairly methodical loo in the haberdashers' to see what seems newest and latest in men's wear. Naturally I have only looked the windows - it would take a Jean d'Arc to go further than that. And even the window-gazing had to be fairly swift, since you are apt to be asked to move on if a policeman se you loitering in Jermyn Street.
ALISON HAIG, FASHION REPORTER IN 'NIGHT AND DAY' MAGAZINE

Truly, the Conservative Party is a wonderful embodiment of good sense, patriotism and honesty.
NEVILLE CHAMBERLAIN, 1931

A remarkable example engineering and planni this building is almost devoid architectural merit. In no pla does it rise above the le of a boiler-hou
HUGH CASSON ON THE N EARL'S COURT EXHIBITION CENTRE, 1

If anyone still feels like buying a new after getting to Earl's Court by road th must have wanted one very badly inde Once you're inside, of course, it's ve pleasant. Earl's Court is immense a glorious, rather like East Anglia w a roof on - but far more peace
REVIEW IN 'NIGHT AND DAY', 1

ELIZABETH

MARGARET ROSE

Through one of the marvels of modern science, I am enabled this Christmas Day to speak to all my people throughout the Empire...
GEORGE V BROADCASTING ON THE NEW BBC EMPIRE SERVICE, 1932

I am beginning to think they must like me for myself.
GEORGE V ON THE HUGE CROWDS CELEBRATING THE SILVER JUBILEE, 1935

After I am dead, the boy will ruin himself in twelve months.
GEORGE V ON HIS SON AND HEIR EDWARD

I have found it impossible to carry the heavy burden of responsibility and to discharge my duties as King as I would wish to do without the help and support of the woman I love.
EDWARD VIII IN HIS ABDICATION SPEECH

Hark the herald angels sing Mrs Simpson's pinched our King.
1936 CHILDREN'S VERSION OF THE POPULAR CHRISTMAS CAROL

the morning of May 12, 1937, pretty, curly-haired little s in purple robes and golden onets stood on a balcony ngside their parents and ved at a cheering crowd. eir Daddy was crowned g of England...they were ng to live in a real palace.
E' MAGAZINE

No, it's your mind, lady!
MAX MILLER, THE 'CHEEKY CHAPPIE'

It is not a question of censorship. It is a question of decency. Some modern books are quite all right, those about travel and those about Sussex, but others ought not to be available.
LONDON 'EVENING STANDARD', 1937

Counsel's opinion was taken as to the definition of a couple 'lying in bed'. Lawyers finally propounded the theory that a couple were 'in bed' when both pairs of feet were off the ground.
CHARLES GRAVES ON FILM CENSORSHIP IN 'THE SPHERE'

It gave the illusion that the participants were threading their way along the ledges of dangerous precipices...
BEVERLEY NICHOLS ON THE TANGO CRAZE

Our true intent is all for your delight.
SLOGAN FOR BUTLIN'S FIRST HOLIDAY CAMP, SKEGNESS, 1937

NIGHT AND DAY

DECEMBER 9 1937   6d

Graham Greene

Nothing over sixpence.
WOOLWORTH'S SLOGAN

I'm afraid it's unlikely that anyone, least of all the BBC, would notice me taking off my hat; but I raise it in the hope that the existence of one grateful listener may be an encouragement to Victor Silvester and his Band to continue to play without the help of vocalists…
I find it difficult to believe that anyone… would miss very much… such a ban would be effective enough if it amounted to no more than forbidding the broadcast of certain rhymes, e.g. Baby: Maybe, Moon: Soon, Remember: December, Blew: Yew…
JOHN HAYWARD IN
'NIGHT AND DAY' MAGAZINE

Of Toscanini there is as usual little to say. Either you think him the greatest conductor alive or else you don't, in which latter case you're wrong.
CONSTANT LAMBERT IN
'NIGHT AND DAY' MAGAZINE

It will chill you and fill you with fears. You'll find it creepy and cruel and crazed.
'THE NEW YORK TIMES' ON
THE FILM 'DRACULA', 1931

I am speaking to you from the Cabinet Room at 10, Downing Street. This morning the British Ambassador in Berlin handed the German government a final note stating that unless we heard from them by eleven o'clock that they were prepared to withdraw their troops from Poland a state of war would exist between us. I have to tell you now that no such undertaking has been received and consequently this country is at war with Germany.
NEVILLE CHAMBERLAIN
SEPTEMBER 1939

The Home Office announ
that the designing of gas ma
has been difficult but this
been surmounted
production is now in ha
GOVERNMENT ANNOUNCEMENT,

Players Ple
CIGARETTE ADVERTISEMENT,

Bye Bye Blues

Words & Music by Bert Lowe, Chauncey Gray, David Bennett & Fred Hamm.

I got a big sur-prise, when I saw you smile.

I nev-er dreamed that it could be.

But now I re-al-ize since I saw you smile,

There's on-ly hap-pi-ness for me. So,

Bye Bye Blues,_____ Bye

Bye Blues._____ Bells ring,

birds sing, Sun is shin-ing, no more

Falling In Love Again

Music & Original Words by Friedrich Hollander.
English Words by Reg Connelly.

The Blue Angel was the 1930 German film that brought international fame to Marlene Dietrich. Its decadent setting in the sleazy night-clubs of pre-war Germany was revolutionary in its time. The songs, by Friedrich Hollander, captured the world-weary cynicism of the time. And one - 'Falling in Love Again', with English words by Reg Connelly - became a standard.

Tempo di valse andante

I of-ten stop and won - der why I ap-peal to men,

how ma - ny times I blun - der in love and out a-gain.

They of - fer me de - vo - tion, I like it I con - fess,

On The Sunny Side Of The Street

Words by Dorothy Fields. Music by Jimmy McHugh.

Where The Blue Of The Night Meets The Gold Of The Day

Words & Music by Roy Turk, Fred Ahlert & Bing Crosby.

Bing Crosby was one of many stars of The Big Broadcast, a 1932 film musical revue. The plot concerned a failing radio station that was saved by the intervention of a series of stars. Bing co-wrote his own song 'Where The Blue Of The Night Meets The Gold Of The Day' and it became his signature tune. The other writers were lyricist Roy Turk and composer/arranger Fred E. Ahlert.

VERSE

Why must I live in dreams_____ of the days that I used to know?_____

Why can't I find real peace of mind, and re - turn to the

Wrap Your Troubles In Dreams (And Dream Your Troubles Away)

Words by Ted Koehler & Billy Moll. Music by Harry Barris.

Harry Barris, a former member of Paul Whiteman's vocal group The Rhythm Boys in the Twenties, appeared in many films, and led his own dance band. In 1931, with Ted Koehler and Billy Moll he created the song 'Wrap Your Troubles In Dreams'. It was featured in the films Top Man (1943) and Rainbow Round My Shoulder (1957), the latter featuring singing star Frankie Laine.

In slow rhythmic tempo

VERSE

What price hap-pi-ness? What price hap-pi-ness? Who can truth-ful-ly say? But for ev-'ry share, with tears we pay.

Love is hap-pi-ness! I've had hap-pi-ness,

But it end-ed one day, Now I look at life a diff-'rent way.

CHORUS

When skies are cloud-y and grey, They're on-ly grey for a day, So wrap your trou-bles in dreams And dream your trou-bles a - way. Un -

27

29

Underneath The Arches

Words & Music by Bud Flanagan.

'Underneath The Arches' was written by one half of the comedy duo (Bud) Flanagan and (Chesney) Allen. Both were seasoned musical performers before their first performance together in Birkenhead where they first performed their signature tune. It was used as the title song of their 1937 film, and was also the name of a successful tribute show just a few years ago.

The Ritz I nev-er sigh for, the Carl-ton they can keep, there's
I don't en-vy oth-ers the com-forts of a home, for

on-ly one place that I know, and that is where I sleep.
there's one place where I can rest, when I've no wish to roam.

CHORUS

Un-der-neath the

30

arch - es,_____ I dream my dreams a - way,_____ un - der- neath the

arch - es,_____ on cob - ble-stones I lay,_____ ev - 'ry night you'll

find me,_____ ti - red out and worn,_____ hap - py when the

day - light comes creep- ing, her- ald- ing the dawn. Sleep - ing when it's

I'm Gettin' Sentimental Over You

Words by Ned Washington. Music by Geo. Bassman.

Ned Washington and George Bassman wrote 'I'm Gettin' Sentimental Over You' in 1932. Washington was a popular lyricist, contributing to stage and screen successes from the Twenties to the Sixties. Composer George Bassman was an arranger for films, and recordings. 'I'm Getting Sentimental Over You' was adopted as his signature tune by bandleader Tommy Dorsey.

love, now I must ad-mit that love is all I'm think-ing of.

Won't you please be kind, and just make up your mind, that you'll be sweet and gen-tle, be gen-tle with me?____ Be-

cause I'm sen-ti-men-tal ov-er you.____

1. (opt. D.%.)

2.

Don't Blame Me

Words & Music by Jimmy McHugh & Dorothy Fields.

Written in 1933, 'Don't Blame Me', by Dorothy Fields and Jimmy McHugh, was featured in MGM's Dinner at Eight with Jean Harlow, and Lionel and John Barrymore among its dinner guests. In 1979, the song made its Broadway début in the burlesque musical Sugar Babies, which starred Mickey Rooney and Ann Miller - who subsequently brought the show to London.

1. Ev-er since the luck-y night I found you___ I've hung a-round you,___ just like a fool
2. I like ev-'ry sin-gle thing a-bout you___ With-out a doubt you___ are like a dream.

Fall-ing head and heels in love like a kid out of
In my mind I find a pic-ture of us as a

school
team.

My poor heart is in an aw-ful state now_____ But it's too
Ev - er since the hour of our meet - ing_____ I've been re -

late now_____ to call a halt.
peat - ing_____ a sil - ly phrase

So if I be-come a
Hop-ing that you'll un - der -

nui - sance
stand me

it's all
one of

your
these

fault!
days.

Don't blame

me
for fall-ing in love with you
I'm un-der your spell but

Stars Fell On Alabama

Words by Mitchell Parish. Music by Frank Perkins.

Salem, Massachusetts-born Frank Perkins was responsible for the music for a few choice songs. As a conductor/arranger, he lived in Hollywood, working on June Haver and Doris Day films. In 1934 he collaborated with Louisiana's Mitchell Parish on 'Stars Fell On Alabama'. The many recordings of this song include a classic by Billie Holiday.

Moon-light and mag-no-lia, star-light in your hair, all the world a dream come true,

did it real-ly hap-pen, was I real-ly there, was I real-ly there with you?

CHORUS

We lived our lit-tle dra-ma, we kissed in a field of white, and stars fell on A-la-ba-ma last night. I can't for-get the gla-mour, your eyes held a ten-der light, and stars fell on A-la-ba-ma last night. I nev-er planned in my i-ma-gi-

41

nation— a si-tu-a-tion— so hea-ven-ly,— a fai-ry land where no one else could

en-ter,— and in the cen-tre— just you and me, dear; my heart beat like a

ham-mer, my arms wound a-round you tight, and stars fell on A-la-

ba-ma last night. night.—

42

My Very Good Friend The Milkman

Words by Johnny Burke. Music by Harold Spina.

New York-born Harold Spina collaborated with California born lyricist Johnny Burke, who was of Irish extraction. 'My Very Good Friend The Milkman' was a hit for larger-than-life singer/pianist Thomas 'Fats' Waller who had the honour of making this song his own. Its joyous, sly ebullience was ideally suited to Waller's bubbly personality.

Cer-tain peo-ple of my ac-quaint-ance Seem ve-ry con-cern'd a-bout you and me. They're

try-ing to be nice. They're go-ing out of their way. They of-fer me ad-

vice; There must be some-thing in what they say._____ My ve-ry good friend the

East Of The Sun (And West Of The Moon)

Words & Music by Brooks Bowman

Brooks Bowman is one of the forgotten men of music, whose reputation rests on two songs, 'Love And A Dime' and 'East Of The Sun (And West Of The Moon)'. The latter was written in 1935, and has enjoyed memorable recordings by Frank Sinatra with Tommy Dorsey, The Inkspots, Peggy Lee, Lee Wiley and Dinah Shore.

Pennies From Heaven

Words by John Burke. Music by Arthur Johnston.

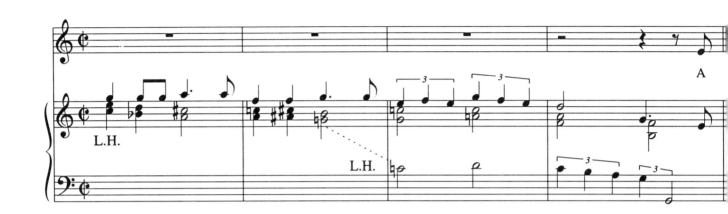

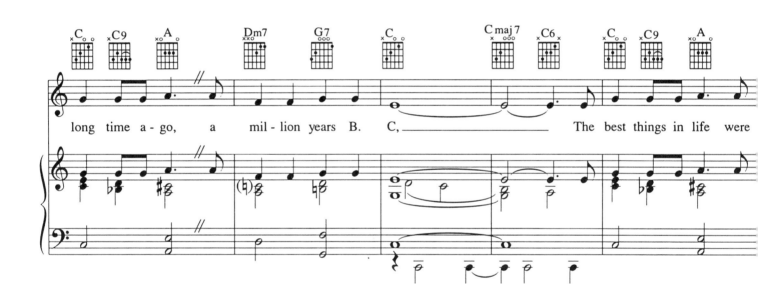

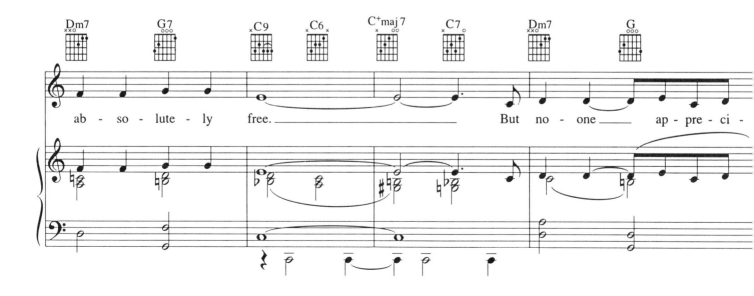

In The Chapel In The Moonlight

Words & Music by Billy Hill.

The Touch Of Your Lips

Words & Music by Ray Noble.

Moderately Slow with expression

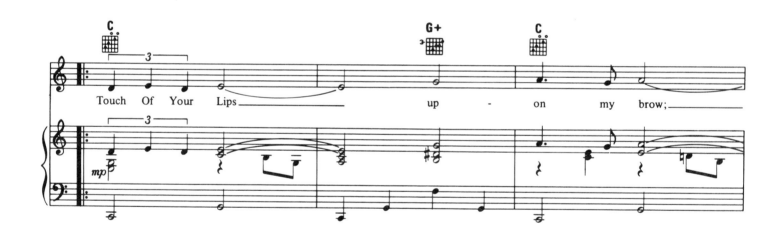

Touch Of Your Lips _____ up - on my brow; _____

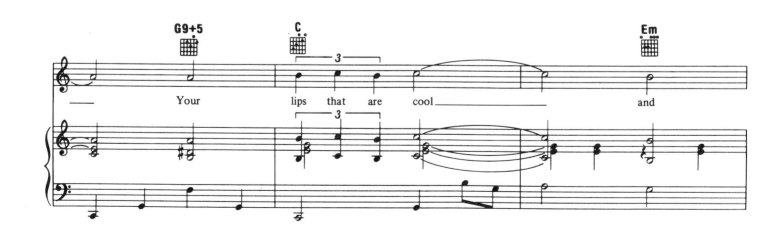

_____ Your lips that are cool _____ and

love in your eyes   a - shine;

And   now   at   last   the mo - ment di -

vine,   The   Touch Of Your Lips   on

mine. The mine.

The Way You Look Tonight

Music by Jerome Kern. Words by Dorothy Fields.

Swing Time, one of the finest of all Fred Astaire-Ginger Rogers pictures, featured Fred as a gambler/dancer, Ginger a dance instructress. At one point, Fred serenaded Ginger (who was off-screen in another room shampooing her hair). Music for the song was written by Jerome Kern and the lyrics were provided by Dorothy Fields. 'The Way You Look Tonight' deservedly won the Oscar for best song of its year.

Some day, when I'm aw-fly
love - ly, with your smile so

low, when the world is cold, I will feel a
warm, and your cheek so soft, there is noth-ing

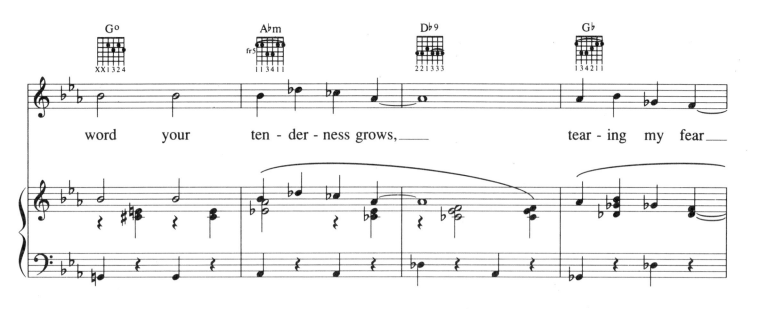

word your ten - der - ness grows,_____ tear - ing my fear_____

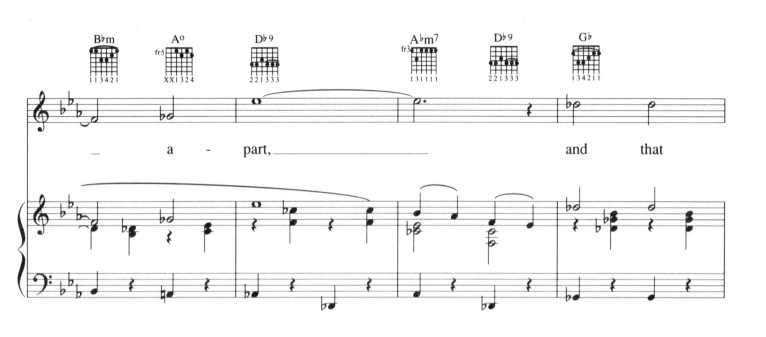

_____ a - part,_____ and that

laugh that wrink - les your nose_____ touch - es my

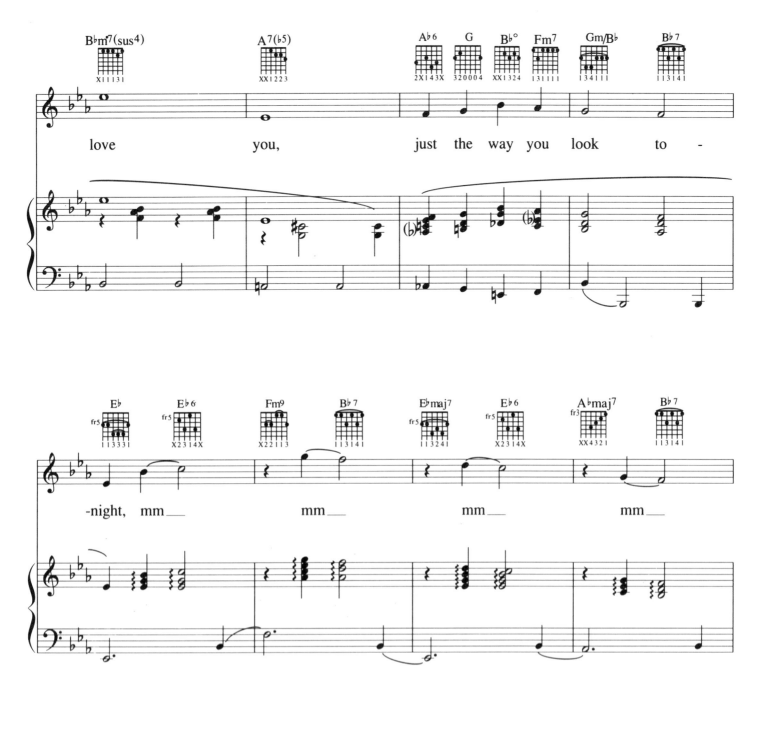

love   you,   just the way you look   to -

-night,   mm__   mm__   mm__   mm__

just the way you look   to - night._____

An Apple For The Teacher

Words by Johnny Burke. Music by James V. Monaco.

Although the pleasant 1939 Bing Crosby film musical The Star Maker dealt with the life of composer Gus Edwards, the man who discovered Eleanor Powell and Eddie Cantor, it included only one of his own songs. The hit song was the newly composed 'An Apple For The Teacher' by two of Crosby's favourite writers, Johnny Burke and James V. Monaco.

You're so-phis-ti-cat-ed, I am too na-ive;
This is no sug-ges-tion, this is no ad-vice;

Well, let's play the game that way if that's what you be-lieve: An
This is just an-oth-er way of be-ing ve-ry nice: An

ap-ple for the teach-er,—— that seems the thing to do,——
ap-ple for the teach-er,—— will al-ways do the trick,—

be - cause I want to learn___ a - bout ro -
when you don't know your les - son in a -

mance from you.___ An ap - ple for the teach - er___ to
rith - me - tic.___ An ap - ple for the teach - er___ will

show I'm meek and mild,___ if you in - sist on
meet with great suc - cess,___ if you for - got to

say - ing that___ I'm just a prob - lem child.___ You'll get all my at -
me - mor - ise___ the Get - tys - burg___ ad - dress.___ A lit - tle bit of

63

64

All The Things You Are

Music by Jerome Kern. Words by Oscar Hammerstein II.

Very Warm For May opened on Broadway in November 1939, closing the following January. May was the heroine, chased by gangsters - hence it was very warm for her! The show contained one of the finest songs of that - or of any - year, 'All The Things You Are', which subsequently featured in the 1944 film Broadway Rhythm.

Moderately, with expression

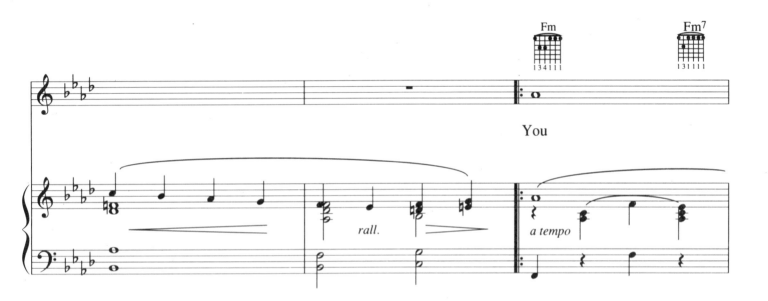

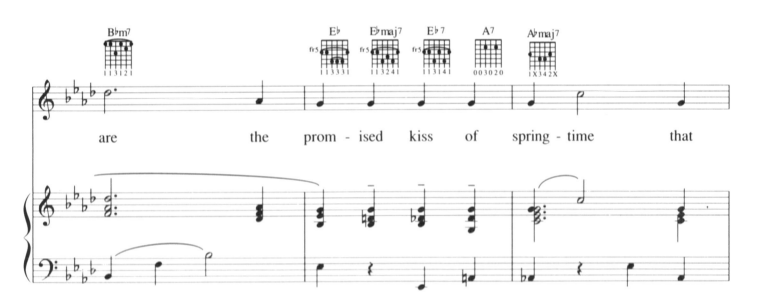

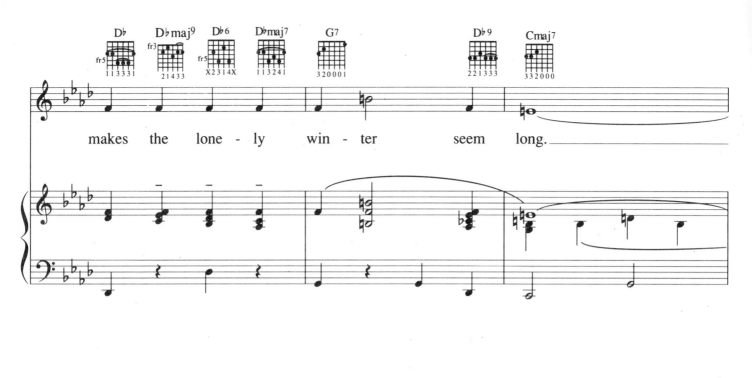

makes the lone - ly win - ter seem long._____

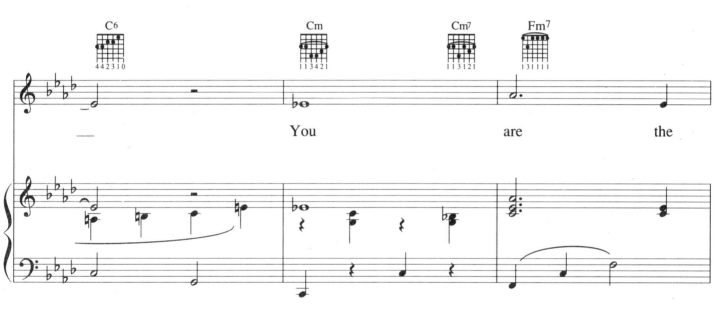

_____ You are the

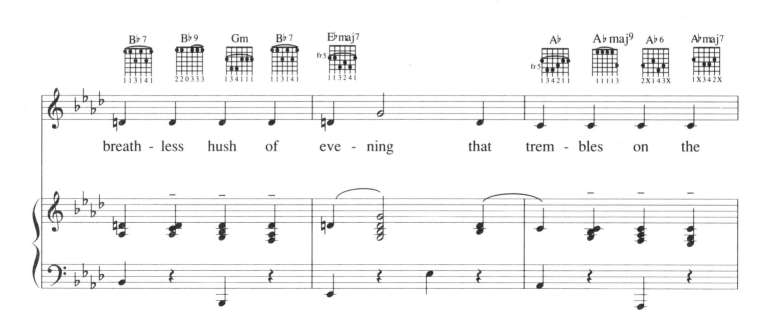

breath - less hush of eve - ning that trem - bles on the

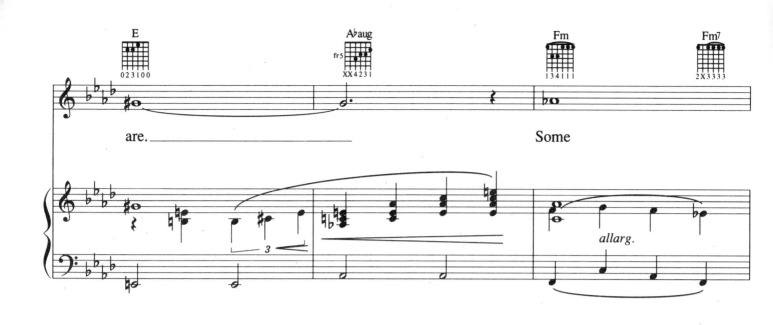

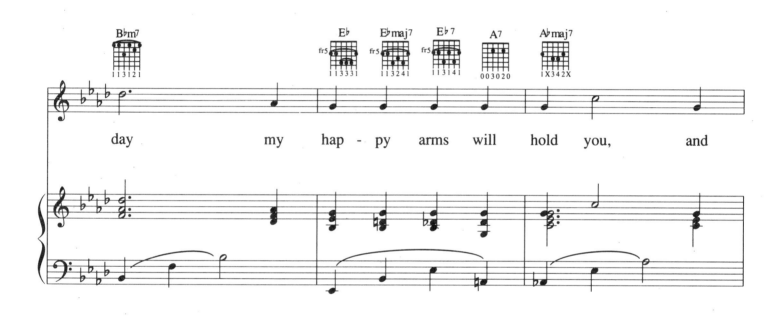

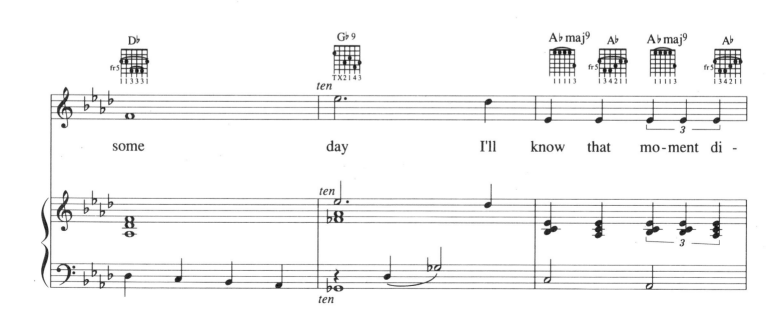

South Of The Border

Words & Music by Jimmy Kennedy & Michael Carr.

'South Of The Border (down Mexico Way)' is a British song from 1939, written by the well-known team of Michael Carr and Jimmy Kennedy who were separately and together responsible for some of the best known novelties and romantic ballads of the 30s and 40s. It was not only a British hit; Bing Crosby also made a memorable hit recording of the song.